Wild Harmony

WILD HAR

by William O. Pruitt, Jr.

NICK LYONS BOOKS

MONY Animals of the North

Drawings by William D. Berry

Nick Lyons • Peter Burford, Publishers

Printed in the United States of America

10 9 8 7 6 5 4 3 2 1

Library of Congress Cataloging-in-Publication Data

Pruitt, William O. (William Obadiah), 1922-
  Wild harmony.

  Reprint. Originally published: New York :
Harper & Row, 1967 under title: Animals of the
north.
    1. Taiga ecology—North America.   2. Animal
ecology—Arctic regions.   I. Title.
QH102.P72   1988   574.5'2643   88-26723
ISBN 1-55821-008-3

Contents

Acknowledgments

These lives of northern animals could never have been written without constant inspiration and help from my wife, Erna, who stoked the fires and made the bread while I was wandering on snowshoes through the forest, and who made the correct critical comment or asked the precise, clarifying question during the writing and proofreading of the rough drafts. I am grateful to the publishers of *Harper's Magazine*; to the Curtis Publishing Company, publishers of *Holiday*; to Abbott Laboratories, publishers of *What's New*, to Purnell and Sons, Ltd., publishers of *Animals*, for permission to reprint articles which appeared originally in their journals. I am deeply grateful to John Macrae of Harper & Row for his skillful and perceptive editing and for never losing faith.

Any appeal these stories have is due to the sensitive and accurate drawings by William D. Berry.

This book would never have been written without the financial support and facilities of the University of Oklahoma during my visiting professorship from September 1963 to June 1965. I am particularly grateful to Dr. Cluff E. Hopla, chairman of the Department of Zoology, for arranging my stay at the University of Oklahoma and for his friendship.

I am also grateful to the Memorial University of Newfoundland, in particular Dr. Frederick A. Aldrich, for support during the final stages of completing the manuscript.

WILLIAM O. PRUITT, JR.

St. John's, Newfoundland
1 April 1966

Wild Harmony

Prologue

Almost every boy, especially if he lives in a rural environment in the temperate zone, has dreams of a life in the Great North Woods. In popular literature the picture of the North Woods, or the taiga, is that presented by the hunting stories, adventure yarns, or tourist promotion advertisements—a land teeming with moose, caribou, and grizzlies, a place where the misfit human being can make a quick fortune trapping mink, marten, white fox, or other valuable fur.

Nothing could be further from the truth. The taiga is, in fact, quite poor in terms of meat production per acre. Not only is it poor, but the ability of the plants and animals to withstand exploitation is very low.

The ultimate factor on which all life, both plant and animal, depends is the sun, which is the source of all energy in two forms—heat and light. The tropics receive more of this energy than do the temperate latitudes, and considerably more than the poles. The result is that the tropics can support the greatest concentration of life in a given area and the poles the least. This life can, of course, be in the form of a thousand mice or one moose—as long as the biomass, or weight of living material per unit area, is the same.

In the tropical rainforest the available energy is divided among an almost unbelievable variety of animals. In the temperate forests the number of different kinds of animals is smaller, while in the far north it is reduced even more.

The sun's energy works in a number of ways, but one of the most important is in creating vegetable life—a leaf or stem or flower or fruit. Then along comes a plant-eating animal and converts part of this sunshine energy into meat. Eventually a meat-eating animal eats the plant-eating animal and so gets his share of the original sunshine. This transfer of the sun's energy is known as a food chain. The many interlocking food chains in nature become a food web. In the tropics there are vast numbers of different kinds of animals and the food web is incredibly complex. Farther north, the food webs become progressively less complex until in the Far North they consist of two or three kinds of plant-eating mammals, one or two meat-eaters, and one or two scavengers.

The entire system is known technically as an *ecosystem*. Once one is accustomed to looking at the world in terms of ecosystems it is easier to see how all living things are inextricably tied together. We can also see why the northern ecosystems are less productive than those of the tropical or temperate zones. Less energy input, less plant output; less plant input, less animal output.

Such ecosystems are termed fragile by comparison with the deciduous forest ecosystems, for example, which are relatively tough. The idea of fragility is difficult to envisage if one's outlook is restricted to the stiffening cold of a taiga winter night or the crashing, squealing, and thundering of great ice blocks tossed in the spring breakup of a taiga river. Nonetheless it is fragile, precisely because of the overwhelmingly powerful environment.

If all this is true, then what has been the basis for the stories about the North Woods teeming with game? Probably the stories have originated because most of the observers (and subsequent storytellers) came from parts of the temperate zone long inhabited and devastated by man. The raconteur probably came from eastern North America (or perhaps western Europe), a land where the elk had long vanished, where the woodland bison was not even a memory, where the only wild ungulate was the tiny whitetail deer. When this man encountered moose, especially a cow with twin yearling calves, of course he was thoroughly impressed with the amount of meat on the hoof. When an early trapper returned in the spring with a fabulous catch of fine fur and told his story, he omitted a footnote. His trapline was probably in a region never before touched by white man, and the region undoubtedly took many years to recover from his fabulous catch.

These facts of taiga life were not apparent to my wife and me when we moved north in 1953. And to the average citizen of a northern city, say Fairbanks or Yellowknife—the man who fights mosquitoes in the summer and struggles to keep his car running through the taiga winter—the idea of a fragile ecosystem would be laughable indeed. The concept became clear to me only after some years of sampling mouse populations, of counting plants, of counting the rings on spruce stumps. It was thrust into sharp focus when I encountered the vast reaches of fire-decimated caribou winter range in northern Saskatchewan. The fragileness of the taiga ecosystem has become even clearer as, in the years since statehood in Alaska, we have seen the rate of exploitation increase.

After I began to understand the mechanisms of the taiga

3

ecosystem it also became evident that most of modern man's activities in the taiga depended on rationales rooted in the errors of attempting to extrapolate temperate zone traditions and techniques to the subarctic. We saw the pitiful results of applying the archaic homestead laws to interior Alaska and the chain-linked disasters that followed unrestrained prospecting and exploitation of minerals in the Canadian taiga. These rationales actually have their start in lack of knowledge of plain old-fashioned natural history. In temperate regions there are several hundred years' accumulation of basic natural history data on the animals and plants of the biota. In the "modern period" we have built on this base and gone far beyond it. But in the taiga we lack this pool of basic information. Thus we may have considerable recently acquired information on, say, thermoregulation or hematology of redbacked voles, while at the same time we still lack a good picture of their patterns of reproduction, their cyclic fluctuations in numbers, their nests, their longevity in nature, and other basic biological attributes.

One important facet of the taiga which has been virtually ignored in North America is its potential as a teaching laboratory. Here in the northern forest we can see the direct effects of physical factors on organisms, we can unravel the simplified food web and examine the component food chains, we can see and experience directly the effects of seasonal changes in light. A number of ecological principles are put on display in graphic clarity. In the taiga, students of ecology can easily grasp the fundamental concepts of the science as they are laid bare around them. This role as a teaching laboratory may well turn out to be the most important use man can make of the taiga; for in the overcrowded and contaminated world of the future, ecology will assume a greater and greater eminence as the central pillar of human survival. Just as inland

4

universities today require doctoral candidates to spend time at a marine station, I visualize the time when temperate-zone universities will require them to take courses at a taiga biological station. But time runs out; in all the North American taiga there is today not a single area held inviolate from exploitation and dedicated to basic biological research, much less as a teaching laboratory.

This book is an effort to project ourselves into the voles' tunnels, to see how the red squirrel and spruces are symbiotically entwined, to pad with the lynx along a hare's trail; in short, to experience and appreciate the taiga world through the senses of the animals themselves. I firmly believe that such appreciation is a necessary prerequisite to the more intensive ecological research which must follow.

Traveling Tree

A hundred yards from the high outside bank of a meander of Alaska's frozen Chena River, a massive white spruce grew. It was mid-March; the sun swung high across the sky. The long subarctic winter had broken and strong winds occasionally moaned through the taiga and caused the tips of the spruces to sway and vibrate, so that the upper half of each tree was clean of snow although the heavily laden lower branches bent low under the snow's weight. The tip of the giant spruce, heavy with cones, towered like a minaret far above the forest floor. Its drooping cones were purplish, and the needles a dark blue-green against the pale sky and the blinding snow cover.

A flock of white-winged crossbills swirled into the top of the spruce. Like tiny parrots they used their feet and beaks as they clambered cautiously about among the twigs. The birds cracked the cone scales apart with their specialized crossed mandibles and then extracted the seeds with their long tongues. The crossbills were wasteful feeders; cones broke off and rattled down through the branches; seeds dropped out and spiraled down to the snow surface.

One seed happened to land in a pit made by a hare track in the snow. As it hit the side of the track it dislodged a tiny avalanche of snow crystals which slid down over the seed and covered it. Other seeds which remained exposed on the snow surface were soon picked up and eaten by redpolls.

The season progressed and grew warmer. As the snow cover compacted, shrank, and finally disappeared, the seed settled by chance into a break in the feather-moss carpet of the forest floor. Here in the wet mor the seed-coat softened. When the floor warmed sufficiently the seed germinated and put forth a tiny, needly shoot.

Season by season the shoot grew, sending up a "leader" and adding a new whorl of branches every year. The parent tree finally declined in vigor, its branches thinned, and the shade decreased. As more sunlight reached the forest floor it grew warmer and the shoot increased its rate of growth. The shoot grew to a sapling.

On a far-distant rim of the continent a nation was born, and as the new nation struggled for life, the spruce, now mature, stretched taller, its outline becoming that of a long, tapering cylinder. While the trunk could grow upward the roots could not penetrate the soil very deeply because of permafrost. They spread laterally, forming a dense but thin mat just below the surface between the moss and the permanently frozen subsoil.

The base of the trunk grew thick and buttressed. The bark was ashy brown, broken into small checks and plates. Wherever the bark skin was broken or injured there oozed a blob of sticky resin which hardened to a rough-textured gray seal over the wound. This resin, which would in time become known as "spruce gum," had a pungent odor, so penetrating and characteristic that unappreciative woodcutters would come to call these trees "stinking spruce." The living branches emerged from the trunk far above the ground. They were twisted and drooped downward before spraying out into needly paws. The needles stuck out all around the twigs, making each paw prickly to the touch. The terminal twiglets were pendulous, forming a drooping fringe to the branch. Below the living branches persisted dry and dead skeletons of branches. The spruce did not shed its leaves suddenly as deciduous trees do, but there was a constant light rain of discarded needles onto the forest floor beneath the tree. The accumulation of dead needles prevented the feather-mosses and lichens from growing within the circle of branches. Thus the trunk protruded from a soft brown, circular mat of dead needles, sharply delimited from the green and gray of the forest floor.

The cones were borne on the younger growth, drooping from the twigs in the topmost ten feet or so of the tree. The number of cones varied greatly from year to year depending on the complex interactions of temperature, rainfall, and age of the tree.

The seeds in the cones furnished food, as those of the parent tree had done, for flocks of crossbills as well as generations of red squirrels. A succession of Canada jays, ruby-crowned kinglets and varied thrushes built nests and raised broods within the reticulum of the branches. For many years a sequence of tiny Richardson's owls used the spruce as a roost. Here they digested their food and dropped to the base of the trunk a growing pile of regurgitated pellets, each of which contained the indigestible bones and fur of the voles and shrews that comprised their food.

Traveling Tree

Year by year the tree grew while the nation enlarged and sent thrusting fingers westward and then northward. The Chena River still flowed clear; prospectors had not yet burned its watershed, no mines spewed silt into its flow. Each year, as the river moved over its flood plain, the meander looped closer to the spruce. Finally the meander reached the edge of the mat of dead needles and the tree towered above the river bank itself.

One winter, just before the white men arrived in the valley, there was an unusually heavy snowfall. By spring the snow cover lay five feet thick. Spring was late, cold, and cloudy. The snow cover lingered on and on. Then a warm spell struck. The sun, now high in the sky, beat down fiercely and the snow cover swiftly shrank.

Streams of meltwater swept down the slopes and coalesced into sheets of water that flooded over the river ice and undermined its edges. The ice creaked and shuddered as it sought to float.

The thaw and runoff increased. The ice cracked, moved, and broke up.

As the river of ice began to move, a thundering crash arose. Blocks of ice jammed into each other, flipped over, and shattered. Great pressures punched ice blocks into the bank, forcing them deep into the soil. A momentary jam developed. Ice screeched as the blocks slid over each other and were forced upward in a pressure ridge. The jam broke and the ridge moved downstream.

A block slammed against the base of the spruce and stripped off a long section of bark. Another floe, as large as a truck, slid over the first and hit the spruce. The great trunk held firm but the roots, their clutch weakened by the undercutting flood, began to tear. The trunk shuddered, swayed, and tipped. The roots pulled loose from the soil with a great

9

crackling and popping sound which was lost in the tumult of the churning ice. The tree crashed over into the grinding river of ice.

Branches as thick as a man's thigh were sheared off. Twenty-foot strips of bark flailed through the air as the trunk rotated and tumbled. Before the tree had traveled a mile it was reduced to nothing but a great flat mass of gnarled major roots from which protruded a single smooth forty-foot spike.

Sometimes the tree was thrust into the air as if it were a giant flagpole. Sometimes it was buried under the churning mass of ice. The current swept on, past the site where one day Captain Barnett's trade boat would run aground and where the town of Fairbanks would spring up.

Not far below this point the Chena River pushed its ice into a much larger stream, the Tanana. An ice jam developed and a pressure ridge arose. The tree was lifted up as the ridge rose under it. The tree tumbled and rolled down the ridge, coming to rest near the edge of the river.

No subsequent pressure ridge or ice push was large enough to move the tree, so there it remained. The ice moved downstream; open water appeared. Stranded ice blocks melted. Summer arrived.

Traveling Tree

In the years that passed, minor floods washed the gnarled roots but none was deep enough to float the tree.

One spring, again after a long winter of unusually heavy snowfall, the Tanana flooded. The water washed the sand away from the roots of the tree. It floated and moved downstream.

As it drifted along, half submerged, it ponderously turned and rolled. Now it was noticed by men. It was called a "sweeper" and all boats gave it wide berth.

The Tanana flowed into an even larger river, the Yukon, whose flow is the lifeblood of northwestern America. The tree joined other trees that had once grown on the banks of the Pelly, the Lewes, the Donjek, the Sheenjek, the Chandalar, and the Porcupine. The current was swift and the water turbid with suspended silt—"too thick to swim in and too thin to plow."

Several years passed during this portion of the tree's journey to the sea. Sometimes it was stranded on a sandbar and only the next spring flood would lift it. It was frozen into the ice in the fall, released in the spring.

The river banks were no longer lined with spruces leaning over the water; the floating trunk had passed treeline and now the vast open tundra stretched to the horizon. The banks became flatter as the tree floated toward the coast.

One bank disappeared, then the other. Ahead stretched the Bering Sea—gray and heaving—shrouded in the peculiar clouds that gave it the name of the "Smoky Sea." The silt-choked water from the Yukon made a vast stain that spread from the river mouth. The tree still floated in fresh water because the "parcel" of Yukon water remained discrete for several days. Finally the water became brackish, and then salt. Chlorides, phosphates, and manganates penetrated the wood and began to deposit in the wood cells. Fragments of algae lodged and grew in cracks and crevices. Tiny marine plankton and crustaceans congregated in the water next to the tree. Larger crustaceans arrived to feed on the smaller ones.

One day a huge mass pushed through the water beside the tree. A gray whale raised its tongue, forced water out through the baleen fringing its mouth, and swallowed several hundred crustaceans. The whale turned in a tight circle and made another pass through the mass of krill. As the forty-foot bulk swam by the tree it scraped against the gnarled root stubs. The roots, which had been nurtured in the distant soil of interior Alaska, gouged several shallow parallel furrows in the black skin of the whale, which was migrating north from its winter habitat in the warm shallow lagoons of Baja California.

Some of the roots protruded above the water surface. A glaucous gull glided down and roosted on the roots. Once it fluttered off and picked from the water several crustaceans injured by the whale's baleen.

The tree drifted with the current. Its progress in a generally northerly direction along the coast was occasionally arrested by violent storms borne on north winds.

Fall came, then winter. The tree, frozen into the sea ice, acted as a structural brace for the ice that formed around it. Thus it survived the winter unscathed, although its floe was tumbled and churned in the howling chaos of the Bering Sea.

Shortly after the melting of the spring ice a strong south-wind storm coincided with an especially high tide. The tree rode through the heaving waves, which turned into a swell and then into pounding surf. The rising tide sent the surf shooting across a beach to burst against a low beach-bluff. The height of the tide combined with the surf to float the massive trunk and roots across the littoral and up the beach. The roots grounded and the whole mass rocked back and forth, churning the gravel of the beach. A large wave lifted the tree and the roots snagged the edge of the bluff. The mass balanced there. A few minutes later another great wave tipped the tree, and it rolled ponderously over onto the tundra vegetation. The tree was wholly out of water for the first time in many years.

As the summer passed the mass of wood slowly dried; its surface bleached to a soft silvery gray. The Arctic nights became longer; frost turned the tundra to yellow and red. Wind-driven snow eddied, swirled, and drifted around the complex surfaces of the trunk and root stubs.

The tree could be seen for miles, a prominent object rising above the tundra. Soon a white fox discovered it and made it a scent post, a boundary marker of his home territory. He visited it regularly and on each visit sprinkled a few drops of bright orange urine on the drift.

The urine stains on the snow attracted the attention of a young Eskimo traveling by dog team along the coast. The fox was later caught in a trap which the Eskimo set beside the tree and cleverly hid under a thin slab of snow. On his next trip the trapper removed the fox and reset the trap.

Because the tree was such a prominent landmark on the open tundra the next fox that invaded the empty home range also used it as a scent post. He, too, was caught.

During the winter five white foxes were drawn to their deaths at the scent post by the great stranded tree.

The winter following, and for many winters thereafter, the trapper regularly took foxes at the site. The tree became known as his trapsite. This was during the time of good prices for long fur, and over the years the trapsite thus contributed many sacks of flour and sugar and boxes of pilot biscuits to the trapper and his family.

No one else set a trap there. A trapline was sacred property to the Eskimos before their culture was eroded by aggressive "free-enterprise" ideas. By the time the trapper was an old man, fur prices had declined to such an extent that he gave up trapping. But everyone still remembered his exact trapline.

After the trapper's death there was discussion when a young man wanted to cut up the scent-post tree for the wood it contained. Such an action would destroy a productive spot in the environment. Finally the council of elders ruled that the tree could be cut up if part were left to collect winter drifts and function as a scent post for foxes. Fur prices were indeed too low at present to make fox trapping profitable, but who knew when they would rise again? In the Arctic only those who plan ahead survive.

The young man traveled to the tree and, with the aid of several neighbors, sawed it up. The great smooth trunk became a prime timber for his new house. The buttressed base of the trunk above the roots was carefully split. Each split section, with its naturally curving grain, would be fashioned into a wondrously strong bow or stern post for the frame of an umiak. These boat frames, when covered with walrus hide, would account for the capture of many bowhead whales. A burl or wood-canker was carefully removed from the trunk. When split and then carved with a *millik*, or man's curved knife, the almost hemispherical grain of the burl would result in a fine scoop for harvesting the crops of tundra berries.

The mass of gnarled and twisted roots was all that remained intact of the great spruce that once had towered above the subarctic taiga. The young man and his companions wedged the root-mass on edge so that it was once again a prominent landmark on the tundra and would continue to serve as a scent post for white foxes.

Traveling Tree

The wood of the tree would continue to exist for many human lifetimes as scent post, house timber, umiak frame, and berry scoop. Eventually the roots would rot. The house timber, the umiak frames, and other pieces would some day end up as firewood. The carbon, hydrogen, water, and other materials comprising the wood would be released into the atmosphere, perhaps to be incorporated once again into another growing spruce tree.

Sentinel of the Taiga

On the north side of the Tanana River in subarctic Alaska, not far from the spot where the traveling tree grew, lay a low ridge. Past this ridge, many years ago, that fallen spruce had moved amid the crush of the breaking ice. The ridge had steep slopes, but its elevation was insignificant in comparison with the mighty peaks of the Alaska Range which loomed on the southern horizon. On the north side of the ridge, on a spur thrust out into the valley of Goldstream Creek, was a patch of forest that the lumbermen and fires had missed. This patch of forest was real subarctic spruce taiga, the kind that has virtually disappeared from North America. The trees were white spruce, white birch, and an occasional balsam poplar. Rising perfectly straight and tapering for about eighty feet, the spruces had trunks that were twenty to thirty inches in diameter. Far above the forest floor their branches twisted out and down from the trunks. While the birches spread up and out from a clean, white central trunk, the poplars were massive and tall, clear of limbs for most of their height, the thick bark dull gray and broken by deep vertical furrows. The forest floor was a thick, soft mat of feather-mosses, with scattered patches of silvery lichens, and dark green lingenberry plants. The mat surface was hummocky, covering a tangle of logs that lay crisscrossed in all stages of decay.

The mature white spruce is the ecological base upon which the entire taiga community has evolved. One spruce germinated in 1741, the same year that the naturalist Georg Wilhelm Steller stepped ashore on Kayak Island and discovered Alaska for Empress Anna of Russia. At a man's chest height, the diameter of the trunk was twenty-eight inches. The growing tip of the trunk was seventy-eight feet above the soil.

The general outline of the tree was that of a greatly elongated pyramid or a tapering cylinder. Branches of neighboring trees made contact only in the lower half of the tree. Thus the "canopy" formed by white spruces is fundamentally different from, for example, that formed by the globular or urn-shaped deciduous trees in an oak-hickory or beech-maple forest.

Far above the ground, on a needly paw surrounded by cones drooping from the twig above, sat a half-pound bit of animal life. This was a red squirrel, sentinel of the taiga. Although a rodent, he was in many respects more like a bird than a mammal—in his constant twitching activity, in his agility in the dizzying heights of the tree tops, his bright color pattern and fluffy tail, and most of all his dependence on his eyes as the chief sensory windows to his world.

His agility derived from his supple, muscular body, his sharp hooked claws, and his marvelous sense of balance. With a great scratching and a shower of bark fragments, he fre-

quently made a headfirst dash down the trunk of the spruce, turned and scampered up the trunk again, scurried out along a branch to its swaying tip forty to fifty feet above the ground, and then propelled himself in a flying leap, legs and tail outstretched, across five or ten feet of empty space to land on a swaying, springy branchlet of a neighboring tree, whereupon he darted to the trunk, scampered to its top, and announced his arrival there with a ringing, rattling call that reverberated over the treetops.

With such well-developed senses of sight and balance the red squirrel was acutely aware of all that went on around him. Few things escaped his eyes. He noted the flapping flight of a raven on the horizon and the bounding fox far below. His alert signal and scolding alarm call frequently exploded through the taiga. Other mammals such as the moose reacted to his calls and used his sensory windows to supplement their own.

The red squirrel did not wander aimlessly through the taiga but lived in a sharply restricted plot, a home range. This particular individual had a home range encompassing thirty mature spruce trees, nine white birches and one great poplar. In addition, on his home range were six spruce stubs, mature trees broken off about forty feet above the ground by qali, the snow that accumulates on trees.

It is not important to calculate the size of the home range in acres of ground, for his range was three-dimensional. The trunks, the bark, the branches of the trees were just as much a part of his home range as was the forest floor. The home range consisted of a three-dimensional latticework of feeding platforms, resting nests, and travel routes. Sometimes the travel routes were continuous from tree to tree, sometimes they were interrupted by gaps which must be traversed by long jumps. Projecting like turrets above the main reticulum of the home range were the principal food sources, the cone-bearing parts of the spruces. On the forest floor and under it was the lowest level of the home range, a series of runways worn into the surface of the moss and another maze of tunnels under and through the kitchen midden.

In the subarctic taiga red squirrels do not construct such formidable middens as they do farther south, in the Rocky Mountains, for example. Our squirrel had a midden twenty feet long, twelve feet wide, and three feet deep. Over the years, he and his predecessors in his home range had used one feeding platform more than others. The midden formed around this platform from the accumulation of cone scales discarded as the squirrels extracted the seeds. The mass of cone scales had a granular consistency not unlike vermiculite and was thus an excellent insulating material. At some stage in its accumulation the midden became thick enough to influence the soil temperatures underneath, and an ancestral squirrel then began a nest cavity deep within it. Over the years the midden grew larger, the tunnels through it became more complex, and the nest cavity more snug.

Now in September the birch leaves glowed golden, the spruce cones were ripe and a deep purple-red, the days were brilliant and the nights crisp. The red squirrel was active all the daylight hours, clipping cones and letting them fall, rattling and bouncing, through the branches to the forest floor below. Occasionally the squirrel jerked down the trunk to the forest floor and, with many chattering interludes, gathered the cones and buried them in caches within the midden. Some cones were missed, some seeds broke loose and spiraled onto the moss. Most decayed but the occasional seed that germinated and survived past the seedling stage was all that was necessary for reproduction of the slow-growing taiga.

While gathering cones the squirrel occasionally disputed

with a neighbor the exact location of the boundary between their adjacent territories. The boundary was settled—temporarily—after much chattering, mewing, and chasing back and forth across it. Such territorial disputes were deadly serious since possession and defense of a territory were integral facets of the squirrels' behavior, as much a characteristic of the species *Tamiasciurus hudsonicus* as the color of the fur or the pattern of enamel folds of the teeth. They have evolved into such an important quality because a personally held and intimately known home range is necessary for the survival of individuals and thus of the species.

One day an alarm call rang out in the distance. The red squirrel darted to an observation post on a limb that projected over a glade. The alarm calls continued and advanced through the taiga as they were repeated by other squirrels. The red squirrel caught a flash of movement in one of *his* trees on the opposite side of *his* home range. He returned to the trunk, scurried around it, moved down a few feet and out on a pathway-branch leading toward the invader. As he prepared to leap to the next tree he caught a better glimpse of him. It was not another squirrel! But it was of similar size, shape, and suppleness, and flowed along the branches with all the agility of a squirrel. It was a marten, the arboreal weasel that has become specialized for the pursuit and capture of squirrels in their own environment.

The red squirrel had time only to give his alarm call before the chase was on. Up the tree, out along a branch to the next tree, down it to the ground, along a runway, up the next tree. The marten gained. The red squirrel dashed to a very difficult series of pathways where each interchange required a flying leap through space. On the first leap the marten followed. The red squirrel headed up the trunk and out along a branch some sixty feet above the ground, and projected himself off the tip.

Through long familiarity with the spot he knew that if he jumped in a certain direction and twisted violently during the fall, he would land in another tree on a branch tip far below and to one side. He hit the needly paw, which dropped, rebounded, and swayed, but he held on and was safe. The marten peered down, gave an explosive bark, and then retraced his route to the trunk to head off in a different direction. Soon he would encounter a squirrel whose knowledge of his home range travel routes was not quite perfect or whose home range was deficient in escape routes. Then his hunt would be successful.

By the end of September the cones were cut. The birch and poplar leaves fell, forming a splash of yellow under each deciduous tree. Day length decreased perceptibly—at this latitude by seven minutes each day.

Day by day the average temperature decreased. The sun rode lower and lower along the crest of the ridge. In October snow fell and stayed. The forest floor was white, save for a dark snow-free shadow, or qamaniq, under every spruce. Meteorologically speaking, the subarctic winter had not really arrived as yet. The atmosphere was still unstable and winds were frequent enough to keep qali from accumulating. By the end of October, however, the Polar High settled over the region. Day after day was clear and calm. The sky changed from pink to salmon to purple and back again. Occasionally a warm front moved over the region and deposited snow.

The snow cover accumulated on the ground and trees. Because the air temperature had been below freezing since late October the snow lay soft, fluffy, and light. The only changes in it were caused by compression and by the upward flow of heat and moisture from the soil below. On the branches the qali solidified slightly as changes in its crystalline structure were caused by radiant energy from the low-lying sun.

Sentinel of the Taiga

The red squirrel now avoided the tips of the lower branches because here the qali had accumulated more than on the upper parts of the spruces. His movements on the forest floor compacted trails in the api—the snow on the forest floor—from tree base to midden to tree base to feeding platform on a stump. Around the base of the stump, layered in snow, were cone scales discarded during feeding sessions.

One day in early December the light cirrus clouds were blotted out by thick low stratus. The air temperature bounded from −10 to +15 in six hours. Snow began to fall. At first the flakes were large, complex plates, but during the night they changed to smaller and simpler plates. Uncounted billions of them sifted down onto the taiga. Many were retained by the trees, building up the accumulation of qali. Below, the api increased in thickness hour by hour. The walls of the qamaniq became steeper and higher as the api built up.

The next day was gray and featureless, scarcely lighter than a moonlit night. Visibility was zero and the forest seemed suspended, surrounded by gray cotton packing. The snow softly whispered and hissed as it accumulated. Suddenly a fifty-foot spruce, growing slightly out of true vertical, snapped with the load of qali, the break occurring about forty feet up. The broken top wheeled over and fell, and as it fell it dislodged qali from itself and the trees it hit. The additional load of snow broke branches from neighboring trees, and all fell to the forest floor in a blinding cloud of swirling snow. The crackling of broken branches was deadened by the thick snow so that the destruction was virtually soundless. Throughout the forest other trees snapped, branches collapsed, pillars of billowing snow joined the fall from the sky.

Although the air temperature was well within his activity range, the red squirrel lay curled inside his midden nest. The swirling fine snow and occasional falling branches disrupted beyond endurance his world above the snow cover.

At the foot of the hill the limber alders bent lower as their qali load increased. Finally each stem was bent in a flat arc, the tip securely anchored in the api. What was once a bristling array of interwined alder stems, rising ten feet above the ground, was now an open glade with a hummocky snow surface and occasional open tunnels leading into great caves roofed with alder stems and snow.

All through the night the snow came down. Shrubs bowed and were covered, birches and aspens bent their limber branches, spruce branches half coiled and released their loads. Occasionally a spruce, bent out of plumb by qali accumulations in previous years, snapped. The lower branches of some spruces curved downward to the level of the api, transforming the qamaniq into circular caves with the trunk in the center.

During the second night the clouds thinned and rose, the snowfall dwindled and stopped. As the protective clouds drifted away and exposed the heat sink of celestial space, the air soon began to chill until the usual winter air temperatures of ten to fifteen degrees below zero were reached. The short subarctic day dawned brilliant and clear, so that the fresh snow crystals glittered and twinkled.

A great burst of energy exploded the red squirrel into action. He burrowed up through the fresh snow. From tree base to midden to tree base to feeding platform, he re-established his trail system; up one spruce, whisking through another, up to the very tip, to proclaim ownership of his fair land with a ringing, rattling call. All through the taiga echoed these territorial calls as all the members of the squirrel world checked their territorial boundaries and remade their trails after the fresh snowfall.

Far away to the west, over the basin of the Ob' River in Siberia, hung a huge, dome-shaped mass of cold, dry, and dense air. It, too, lost its heat to outer space and got progressively colder. Finally the pressures of global atmospheric circulation started the huge mass moving again. Eastward it slid, over the Cold Pole of Verkhoyansk, the Amur country, Chukotka, above Bering Strait and the Date Line, and over Alaska. Here, pinched between the Brooks Range to the north and the Alaska Range to the south, it rested again.

When the air temperature fell to twenty-five below zero, the squirrels deserted the crisp, glittering world above the snow and retreated into their network of tunnels beneath the snow and in the middens. This was a major change—from the cold, dry, and brilliant world of the raven and lynx to the warm, humid, and dark world of the vole and shrew, from the subarctic to the temperate zone. Only by such a drastic change in habits could the red squirrels exist in the subarctic. Their size and mass decreed no extended exposure to temperatures lower than twenty-five or thirty below. If they were larger and heavier they could withstand lower temperatures, but if they were larger and heavier they could not scamper and leap through the swaying spruce branches as they do.

Over the taiga the air was filled with tiny, glittering ice crystals as the moisture was squeezed from the cooling air. The tiny crystals refracted the light from the low sun and caused rainbowlike parhelia, or sundogs, in the sky. The crystals settled onto the forest, adding to the qali and api. The temperature fell, from thirty to thirty-five to forty below. It stayed at forty-five below for several days. Differential contraction caused a poplar trunk to split with a crack like a rifle shot. The spruce twigs became brittle as glass. Some, already near their breaking point with their qali load, cracked and dropped. More earth-heat flowed away to space and the temperature finally hung at fifty-five degrees below zero Fahrenheit.

At this temperature most animal activity took a different turn. Snowshoe hares, which usually ignored the cold, retreated into the snow caves under the alders. Here they were protected from much of the heat loss by the radiation shield of the snow roof above them. Here, also, they had a good food supply in the alder bark. The red squirrel was virtually unaffected by the deep cold since he had long since retreated to his subnivean nest and tunnels in the midden. If he were forcibly brought to the surface he would not be able to survive the numbing cold for more than a few minutes. The moose fluffed out its fur and turned from blackish brown to gray as each hair became tipped with frost. Every exhaled breath hissed as its moisture froze. When the moose stood feeding in a willow thicket a cloud of ice fog formed over him. As he moved away, crashing through the brittle branches, his trail was marked not only by the deep holes and furrows in the snow but by the hanging cloud of ice fog. The cloud trail slowly drifted downhill as the colder air flowed into the deep valleys and swales.

A grouse walked precariously on the brittle branches of the poplars, pecking buds. When its crop was stuffed, it set its wings and plummeted into the snow, to spend the digestion period down where the heat stress was less. The tiny chickadees huddled inside a thick spruce clump under the qali and fluffed their feathers until their feet disappeared into the ball. The only creatures seemingly unaffected by the deep cold were the ravens, who rowed through the dense air with whistling wing strokes, and the lynx, who padded on floor-mop feet along the hare trails.

Far to the south a great area of low pressure developed. Winds howled over the Gulf of Alaska as the pressure gradient steepened. The northern edge of the low lapped at the south side of the Alaska Range, on the other side of which rode the high. The pressure differential caused winds to blast through the mountain passes. Finally the huge dome of cold, dry air began to slide eastward along the north side of the Alaska Range, into Yukon Territory and northern British Columbia. Warm, moist air spilled through the passes behind it. Streamers of clouds moved north, the temperature rose. The cold snap was broken.

When the air above the snow had warmed to above the critical temperature, red squirrels appeared in the taiga. As they have for aeons, they checked their territorial boundaries, disputed them, proclaimed ownership. They brought spruce cones to the snow surface, shelled them and ate the seeds, adding the cone scales to the midden heaps. As it has for aeons, the sight of fox or lynx sent the squirrels swirling up the spruce trees. Here they perched on tiny branches and shouted their alarm calls—the sentinels of the taiga.

The Voles' World

The scar of the great forest fire was still relatively fresh after half a century. Aspens and birches formed a canopy over the burn, while through the deciduous trees, young spruces thrust upward. The leafy canopy was thin, with many openings through which the sunlight streamed onto the forest floor. Dead leaves of aspen, birch, and willow formed an irregular carpet interspersed with patches of brown and green grasses, feathery green horsetails, and the dark, shining green lowbush cranberry leaves. The flexible woody shoots of highbush cranberry waved above the forest floor.

As the sun moved through the sky the patches of light and heat flickered over the forest floor. Some parts of the floor were in almost continuous light, others in continual shade. The light heated and cooled the forest floor in changing patterns. This was the upper world where the squirrel pursued his three-dimensional life. But below, in the mats of dead and sere leaves under the grassy areas, was a world of tunnels and runways. These runways continued through the litter of

deciduous leaves but were few in the needle litter under the young spruces. The runway system was constructed and maintained by a population of voles. (These small mammals were technically known as *Microtus oeconomus*. Their "official" English name of tundra vole was clearly in error, because they were as common in the taiga as in the tundra.) Voles were inveterate housekeepers; they stored seeds and edible rootlets and were forever cleaning and remaking their runway systems. Thus the Old World name "ekonomka" or "housewife" is more apt. Voles were also asocial; that is, they felt no great urge to contact their fellows. They kept to themselves, each to his own system of tunnels and runways that radiated from the nests to all parts of their home ranges. Where adjacent runway systems intermeshed, the territorial boundaries were clearly marked with scent posts.

As summer passed into autumn the birch and aspen leaves turned gold, then faded and clattered down through the branches. The canopy opened and the sun warmed the forest floor in a brief interlude. Birch leaves speckled the dark green cranberry patches; their yellow contrasted with the brilliant red berries. The maple-shaped leaves of highbush cranberry turned to a red and russet backdrop for their clusters of shining berries. Horsetails made a smoky yellow haze over the forest floor.

The sparkle of the short subarctic autumn faded as a chill rain pattered onto the forest floor. The colors dimmed and the once crisp leaves relaxed and joined their predecessors in the cycle of decay and humus formation. Grass, leaves, and horsetails formed a sopping network over the voles' runways. As the voles foraged and repaired they shook the vegetation and a continuous spray settled onto them. A vole would stop short, shake itself violently, and begin to preen its fur. If its fur became soaked and matted, a vole could not produce enough heat to live. Thus the voles whose home ranges did not provide dry nest-refuges were obliged to increase their food intake to produce more heat. Some individuals could not do this, and they huddled in their sodden nests. Their foraging trips were feeble; they stumbled along the runways, wheezing and gasping as their lungs choked with cellular exudate. These individuals could not stay alert; a fox took some, a lynx took some, as did a boreal owl. As the nights grew longer the temperature dipped lower and lower. Crystals of ice formed on the wet leaves; in shaded spots the ice survived the daylight hours. More crystals formed, they coalesced into sheets and glittering reticula that crackled and tinkled as the voles thrust their way among them.

Now the vegetation was completely enmeshed in the ice lattice, and the soil surface itself began to buckle as crystals grew within. Throughout October the freezing spread deeper, reaching into all crevices and cracks and even penetrating some nests. Some voles died, for forage they must, yet they dared not experience such heat loss for extended periods.

Then came the snow, at first a light dusting that dappled the ground only under the deciduous trees and between the young spruces. This first layer had little effect on the voles' world since it scarcely altered the heat flow gradient from the earth to the air. But the voles reveled in it; their tracks quickly made a network, their runways made tiny trenches and tunnels over and through it. Even when the snow cover thickened the voles continued to trench it and emerged to scamper over its surface.

A series of high-pressure areas moved over the taiga, and the snow increments dwindled. The air temperature fell to well below zero. The snow cover was not thick enough to insulate the earth from the heat sink of the subarctic sky, and the leaf litter froze solidly. Heat flowed upward, sucked from soil, plants, nests, and even voles. On their foraging trips, the voles avoided exposure to the infinite heat sink of the sky, hugging the protective cover of dense, overhanging vegetation. Nonetheless, the metabolic strain was intense, particularly on the older individuals whose fur was ragged and worn thin. Some voles died huddled in their nests, and they soon froze into icy mummies.

Then the cold snap weakened; clouds softened the brittle sky and snow began to fall. The cover thickened and passed the magical hiemal threshold—insulation sufficient to curtail the deadly sweep of heat from the voles' world. This was the true beginning of winter, and the voles solemnized it by abandoning the snow surface. The network of their trails and trenches filled up and was not renewed. But down below, beneath the snow cover, the voles' activity increased and the number of their tunnels grew as the heat flow slackened and the subsnow temperature actually increased, then stabilized at just below freezing.

The voles shunned those parts of their home ranges that were cold to their feet. Consequently, they rarely ventured into the snow shadows or qamaniq under the young spruces, where the thin snow cover did not prevent the escape of the earth's heat. Moreover, the qamaniq were where a lynx frequently crouched in ambush and the scent of the big-footed cat permeated these spots.

Throughout early winter, snowfalls alternated with clear, calm weather. Each snowfall had a different meteorological origin and history, and thus each layer of the snow cover differed from all others in thickness and density. But such complexities did not now concern the voles since their time was occupied with expanding their runway network and consolidating the scent-marked boundaries around the protected areas in their home ranges.

As the nights lengthened to their yearly maximums and the heat received from the sun dwindled to nearly zero, a huge dome of cold, dry air drifted eastward and pressed over the taiga. Heat flowed from the snow surface, the tree trunks, the needles, and the air itself to outer space. An aspen trunk cracked and split as it shrank.

A spruce grouse plunged from a limb and dived into the snow below. Once below the surface it swam several feet through the fluffy mass and then wriggled and compacted a snug cave for itself. The wriggling collapsed the tunnel behind it, and the grouse was tucked into warm snow, surrounded by insulation. Here the grouse could rest throughout the long subarctic night, while the aspen buds in its crop were digested and released their calories of life-heat.

The voles continued their routine of living: several hours' sleep in their nests, then a foraging trip to a food cache, then perhaps an exploration boring a new tunnel through the matted grasses and horsetails to expose a fresh source of food, then back for more sleep. This rhythm of sleep and wakefulness came from within, for here in the subnivean world there was no cycle of light and darkness, no rise and fall of temperature, no moon, no warble of pine grosbeak or hoot of owl to synchronize the voles' activities with the rhythms of the cold, dry, pulsating world above the snow.

Life for the voles continued its routine, even while the high-pressure dome drifted away across the continent and was followed by a thinner mass of warm, moist air. Moisture from the fresh warm air precipitated onto the frigid trunks and branches. Soon all the taiga was in silver clothes of flat, scissile ice crystals. The sudden change in temperature and moisture caused the birch cones to spread open and tiny winged seeds fluttered downward to the snow surface. Under some trees the snow turned sandy-tan with its overburden of birch seeds. Soon the redpolls, chickadees, grosbeaks, and even the Canada jays had the surface covered with their intertwining trails as they hopped and fluttered while feeding on the high-calorie food spread before them.

One day in mid-January the light cirrus clouds were blotted out by thick low stratus. The air temperature bounded from ten below to fifteen above zero in six hours. Snow began to fall. Api, the snow on the forest floor, increased in thickness hour by hour. The walls of the qamaniq became steeper and higher as the api accumulated.

The new snow covered the layer of birch seeds and hid them from the small birds. The added weight of the fresh snow compacted the middle layers of the api. As the crystals squeezed together and broke, the cover creaked and groaned. A foraging vole would stop and huddle, ears twitching, and then resume its errand. The sounds breached the even tenor of life under the snow.

An additional disturbance was the faint scent of birch carbohydrate that occasionally filtered down from above. Some voles dug upward through the layers of snow. One layer was easily tunneled, the next was harder; no two were alike. When a vole reached the seed-rich layer it drove a horizontal drift along it and devoured every seed. Without the traditional scent boundaries to restrain them, some voles encountered their fellows directly. What squeaking and scuffling as the asocial animals repulsed invaders! Thus the voles added a new dimension—height—to their normally two-dimensional lives, and a new complexity to their home ranges.

The life-protecting snow cover also brought with it a source of potential danger to the voles. Ever since the api had gained the hiemal threshold, and the temperature of the soil and humus had stabilized at a scarcely freezing level, bacterial action had continued slowly to break down and decompose the birch and aspen leaves, the grass stems, and the leaves of horsetails. The chemistry of bacterial decay resulted in the formation and release of carbon dioxide gas. Carbon dioxide is a heavy gas, but the constant flow of heat and moisture

34

from the soil up through the snow had kept it from the voles' habitat as soon as it was formed.

But now the dense layers of compressed snow prevented the free escape of this gas. Being heavier than air, it drifted downhill under the api and began to accumulate in hollows and low spots.

As the carbon dioxide concentration rose, the voles that lived in these low spots increased their respiratory rate and began to feel unsure and alert. The result was increased activity and a desire to breathe deeply. The voles could not expand their activity ranges laterally because of the presence of other voles' home ranges alongside theirs. Their tunnels already led upward through the snow to the birch-seed layer and the voles continued them to the snow surface, which overnight erupted with tiny ventilator shafts.

When the warm, moist air that passed upward encountered the zone of severe freezing, some of its moisture precipitated onto the walls of the ventilator shaft, which thus became a tube lined with delicate spicules of ice. From the ventilator shafts rose tiny wisps of steam as the warm, moist, and polluted air flowed out into the cold, dry air above the snow.

In several low places in the forest the carbon dioxide continued to form and accumulate faster than the ventilators could sweep it away. Here the restlessness of the voles became intense. Increased activity brought more frequent contacts, with threats and agonistic displays, rattlings of teeth, and chirring squeaks. One vole, hotly pursued by another, fled up a ventilator shaft, scattering the delicate ice crystals in tinkling disarray. The vole popped onto the surface and scurried away on the yielding snow.

There was a soft rush of air and a great shadow fell upon the snow; the vole gave a squeak as curved talons squeezed its life away. The boreal owl looked around, popped his beak, and flew off with the vole to a young spruce. Scarcely had he finished tearing and eating the carcass when he spied another vole scuttling over the snow surface. The owl pitched out of the spruce and glided to overtake his prey.

Day by day the carbon dioxide under the snow increased and the gas pocket spread, forcing more voles to become restless and wander. The little owl grew fat. Now he produced more than enough body heat to offset the drain to the subarctic air around him. Without the displaced voles for food the owl probably could not have survived the deep cold of winter in this region of the taiga.

The denser layers of snow that impeded the escape of carbon dioxide also slowed the escape of heat from the subsnow world. The resulting rise in temperature was slight, but still sufficient to increase the rate of change in the morphology of the api. At the base of the snow cover, molecules of water vapor escaped from the attenuated tips of crystals and spicules and attached themselves to larger ice surfaces. Thus the already enlarged grains of pukak gained in mass at the expense of smaller and more delicate crystals. The process of recrystallization moved upward through the api and the layer of pukak increased in thickness.

Above the taiga the sun each day climbed higher into the sky. The grip of the Polar High relaxed around its periphery. Low-pressure cells, which in the middle of winter would have slid around the edge of the Polar High, now nibbled at its edges and sucked some of its denser air into themselves. In the taiga the winds increased.

The intensified solar radiation slightly warmed the needly paws of the spruce branches and gently loosened the mass of qali on each. A weak breeze sighed through the spruce tops and set them swaying. High in the apex of one tree a lump of qali slid from its branch and fell. The branch, relieved of the

36

weight, whipped upward and in doing so shook loose the remainder of its load of qali. The lumps of snow struck other branches below and jarred their qali loose. In a few seconds the tree was enveloped in a swirling plume of snow as branch after branch down one side released their burdens of qali. Two branches snapped off and many needles rained down. The lumps of qali thumped onto the api and created moon-like craters on its surface. The broken branches speared the snow cover, and the dislodged needles littered its surface. Tree after tree shed portions of its qali. For an entire afternoon the taiga was hazy with flying snow crystals and noisy with crashings and thumps as branches snapped and qali lumps cratered the api.

The vibrations traveled down through the snow to the voles' world. Columns of delicately poised pukak shattered and collapsed. No voles stirred from their nests during this beginning of the breakup of their world. The vibrations ceased as the sun angled toward the horizon and the remaining qali froze solidly to the needles. Then the voles emerged from their nests to find their carefully constructed runway systems filled with pukak crystals. Clear runways are vital for microtine survival, and the instinct to tidy up a runway is one of the foundations of vole behavior. So the voles dug and scratched and pushed ice crystals until their runways were once again passable.

The increase in subnivean temperature caused several kinds of hardy insects to complete their development. As they hatched or emerged they began a long struggle upward through the layers of snow. When the sun was at its peak they suddenly appeared on the snow surface—myriads of tiny bluish snowfleas, which hopped erratically, and an occasional long-legged, spiderlike, wingless cranefly which progressed with the same agonizing slowness as does a sloth.

When the sun passed the zenith and the air began to chill, the snowfleas collected in the warmest spots they could find. The qali-caused craters in the snow surface suddenly acquired shadows on the wrong sides of their walls. The shadows were actually closely packed thousands of snowfleas congregated on the slightly warmer southwest-facing slopes of the walls of the miniature moon-craters. Each crater's outline was picked out in a living countershadow of bluish gray.

At a spot where a large qali blob had broken through the surface crust there appeared a quivering vibrissae-rimmed snout. A shrew popped onto the snow surface and began to snap up the chill-benumbed snowfleas. Such a trove of food did not appear often. The shrew scuttled over the compacted snow surface, blundered into another snow crater, and scooped up more snowfleas.

When the shrew was satiated it began to probe the hardened snow in an effort to return below the surface. The sun by this time had slid below the trees and the chill had deepened. The shrew's minuscule foreclaws made tiny scratchings as it tried to dig the hardened crust. It ran erratically; frantically and futilely it probed the crust that locked it out of its warm subnivean world. Its movements grew more erratic, and before many minutes had passed it curled into a tiny ball in an effort to conserve its dwindling body heat. Thus it died and froze solid, a tiny speck on the surface of the taiga api.

By the middle of April the flow of heat upward through the snow cover had slackened. Now, indeed, during the day heat flowed downward from the surface, and back again at night. The variations in heat flow increased the speed of recrystallization and soon all the snow below the surface crust was pukak.

The crust itself was now hard enough to support large animals. One day in April a cross-fox passed through the old burn. He trotted along, claws clacking and scratching on the crust. Occasionally he slipped on a steeper and slicker spot and his great fluffy tail whipped as it helped him recover his balance. Suddenly the fox stopped, sat down, and cocked his head. He had entered a zone of delicious smells—voles, whose scents rose all about him. There, a faint squeak, then another. The fox rose slowly, slowly; daintily he extended one front foot. He eased forward until the squeaks seemed to come from directly below.

Then he crouched and jumped high in the air, all four feet tucked together. His full weight thumped onto the crust, which cracked. The fox dug frantically, using his teeth to loosen the slabs of crust and his forefeet to toss them backwards. As he dug down through the snow the pukak loosened and flowed into the hole, nearly covering him. The fox snorted and shook his head to free himself of the cold crystals. Another avalanche of pukak crystals caused him to scramble hastily back to the snow surface. He shook himself and a cloud of pukak crystals tinkled over the crust. Underneath such a shifting, hair-trigger mass the voles were safe.

As the fox clattered away across an open area to try his luck elsewhere, the crust beneath his feet suddenly sank several inches. The collapse spread as does a ripple on a pond and a dull *whoom* rose from all around. Successive booms and collapses accompanied the fox until he reached the cover of the adjacent trees. Here the struts of woody vegetation supported the snow cover and prevented its breakdown.

Day by day the sun reached higher in the sky. When the crust was soft during the day the caribou plowed trails through it, beginning the spring migration that would take them to the high, rocky tundra five hundred or more miles distant. At night when the crust hardened again the caribou's migratory urge declined and the animals fed and rested in a sharply circumscribed area.

Daily the snow cover shrank. The sun's rays heated the

aspen trunks, which re-radiated the energy to the snow around them. Soon each aspen trunk protruded from the north edge of a deep cylinder sublimed through the snow.

Each hare pellet, twig, and needle that lay in or on the snow surface absorbed the heat and re-radiated it to the adjacent snow. Hare pellets sublimed vertical tubes down through the crust. Twigs and needles made irregular cavities as they sank below the surface.

In the qamaniq, under the sweeping lower branches of the young spruces, the air temperature rose markedly. The thin snow layer sublimed, disappeared, and exposed the dark needle litter. The qamaniq now became hothouses for animals which depended on outside heat for energy. Here spiders stretched their legs; mosquitoes, groggy from hibernation, emerged and tried a few feeble flights; carpenter ants began to re-establish their trails. Thus the qamaniq, which during the winter had been shunned by most living things, now became the center of animal activity. The quickening invertebrate life attracted chickadees and redpolls, and even a rare brown creeper. From soggy tunnels under the shrinking snow cover, voles came to the qamaniq to roll and wriggle in the dry, warm needle duff.

Now it no longer froze at night and the snow cover, grown old and granular, pitted, and vacuolated, was saturated with its own juice of decay. All was wet: the moss, dead leaves, grass stems, shriveled horsetails, all exuded water and dripped. The vole population, by now decimated to only a vague outline of its autumnal strength, retreated once more from the low spots, this time as they became sumps of icy water. Just as one of the crises of the voles' lives came in autumn, now in spring there was another. The protecting snow cover was no more, all that remained was a soggy travesty of api. Yet the voles' tunnels and nests were wet and virtually useless as insulation. Winter had retreated only to just beyond the hill and could still suck the heat from the taiga in a last defiant gesture. If this should occur, the voles' world would be transformed into an ice-sheathed prison in which food supplies, already scarce, would be locked away and through which no new tunnels could be forced; the vole population would be decimated further.

But the snow cover continued to shrink; then it disappeared from the south-facing slopes and the open spots. It lingered in the deepest shade, and finally even from there it was gone. The moss and vegetation dried with the increasing heat of the sun. The vole population had survived.

The Hare's World

Winter was over, breakup had come and gone, and spring flooded over the taiga. The axis of the earth tilted more and more toward the sun. Noon by noon the sun hung higher in the sky, and day by day it rose farther to the north, rolling along the horizon before it began its climb to the zenith. The soil was warm where it was exposed to the midday heat, but in the shade of the spruces, where the feather-mosses grew thick and springy, it was still winter and ice crystals clung to the bases of the moss plants. Early in the morning and late in the afternoon, the subarctic sunlight angled under the trees, casting long shadows, but the rays lacked heat at these times of the day.

On a south-facing slope where the aspens and birches grew thick in an old burn, the light that reached the forest floor was tinted a yellow green, partially filtered through the new and expanding translucent leaves of birch, aspen, and alder. The delicate tracery of twigs and the areas of colors fashioned a glowing design.

The *Ledum* shrubs were not in bloom; they needed more heat on their roots. But their evergreen leaves, dull green on top and fuzzy brown below, were at work using the sunlight to manufacture food for future blossoms.

The wind swayed the tips of the spruces on the hilltop. From down the hill, where the slope flattened out in the black spruce muskeg, came the sucking, squishing sounds of a moose walking over the soggy soil. It was a cow returning to her newborn calf, which lay curled in a patch of sunlight in an alder thicket.

Big bluebottle flies flailed through the air, as did whining mosquitoes. These insects were of the hardy breed that survive the subarctic winter as adults by hibernating in bark crevices or splintered trunks. Although the mosquitoes were bloodsuckers, they were great, slow-flying *Culiseta* and not the small, persistent *Aedes* which would hatch in swarms in the summer.

On this south slope, beneath the trunks of two small aspens that had died and fallen crossed, was a clump of dry, brittle branches and strips of peeling, dead bark, suspended from the trunks. Under the mat of branches, in the dried grass and leaf litter, was a shallow scrape about eight inches square. The depression led by a tiny ramp to the surface. Within the shallow scrape, snuggled together, lay six very young snowshoe hares.

The hares were perfect miniatures of their parents—bright-eyed, alert, and fully furred—but still unsteady on their feet. It was not need for warmth or the desire for company that caused them to snuggle in a heap. By huddling they presented only a single fuzzy surface to the cloud of mosquitoes that hung just above the nest. Periodically the furry mass heaved and wriggled as one of the outside hares squirmed into the center of the mass and took respite from the mosquitoes which attempted to infiltrate its fur.

Huddling was thus the hares' defense against mosquitoes. After their fur grew thick enough to prevent mosquito penetration, and after they had developed sufficient muscular coordination to brush mosquitoes from their eyelids, the mass of young hares would break up. Each would go its own separate way, never to meet again except as strangers.

Several times a day the mother hare visited the nest, and later her scattered brood, to clean their fur and to suckle them. The young hares grew fast and soon began to assert their individuality by growling and striking at their littermates.

When the litter broke up one young hare tumbled through the dense growth of *Ledum* for nearly a quarter of a mile. He finally stopped, panting, under a small spruce that grew in a thicket of alders. He reached out his head, clipped a juicy young shoot of fireweed and drew it into his mouth with deft manipulations by his sensitive lips. As he chewed, his jaws rocking from side to side, the fireweed shoot waggled back and forth until it disappeared to become rabbit meat. After eating several shoots the young hare began to dress his fur. He licked all the parts he could reach with his mouth, and scratched all the others. He carefully drew his ears down over his face and ran his foreclaws over them. He lifted first one huge hind foot, then the other, and spread wide the toes in order to clean the fur. After all his fur was preened and fluffed he stretched, yawned, and napped. He never knew that while he was napping death brushed close. A fox trotted by, following a small, twisting trail through the dense underwood. By chance the young hare's scent trail was not intercepted by the fox.

The Hare's World

The hare ventured away from the small spruce for feeding, but he usually returned to its shade to pass the heat of the day. As his home range expanded he established other resting spots throughout it. One spot was on the opposite side of the alder clump, close under the protection of a leaning, moss-covered stem of alder. Another place that eventually became his favorite as the days cooled toward autumn was on top of a large rotting log of paper birch. The trunk was partly hollow but the mottled gray bark was sound and tough. The hare liked the feel of the bark under his feet. The log lay where the great birch, in falling, had ripped a break in the forest canopy. Thus it was in full sunlight for several hours every day.

Sometimes, after having basked motionless in the sun for an hour, the hare would drum with his huge hind feet on the resounding birch log. The drumming noise rolled over his patch of taiga, sounding for all the world like the springtime wing-drumming of a ruffed grouse.

One day the hare encountered a scent strange to him. It clung to the leaves alongside one of his trails. When he first encountered it his ears went back and pressed flat along his neck, while his head tipped upward until his nose was elevated above the horizontal. A subconscious tensing of chest muscles forced air from his lungs, causing him to growl. The scent that evoked the reactions was that of another hare. The posture and growl were instinctive expressions of antagonism toward a hare invading his home territory. He followed the scent trail aggressively, but it continued on beyond the boundary of his range and the hare turned back toward the center of his familiar territory.

The hare's home range encompassed some ten acres. Most of it was in the old burn, but one border of it was formed by a stand of large white spruce that was underlaid by a thick carpet of feather-mosses. This stand was a remnant of the original forest. The hare rarely ventured into the unburned spruce taiga, principally because of the lack of young deciduous underwood there.

Within the hare's range were many small spruces, young birches and willows, and a dense tangle of Ledum undergrowth. Several areas lacked Ledum, and here the ground was covered with greenish-gold mosses and the shining dark green leaves of lowbush cranberry. Everywhere were feathery green horsetails.

Several large clumps of alders grew on the hare's home range. The alders furnished shade in this season of the year, and in the coming winter would be an important source of food. They were important to future generations of hares also, since they fixed atmospheric nitrogen and stored it underground, where it enriched the soil and thus replenished the nutrients that passed into hare meat.

The hare now had developed a tangled skein of trails and runways over its home range. To a human being the pathways would have been invisible since they were delimited primarily by scent; but the hare knew them perfectly in all their turns and obstructions. Other creatures of the taiga also knew— and used—the hare's trails. The red squirrels frequently dashed along them. During the dusky hours that passed for summer nights in the subarctic forest, the red-backed voles would patter along the hare's trails.

Each visitor left a trail of scent and the hare recognized them all. Other scents than those of squirrel and vole swirled and drifted around the hare, scents of shrew and moose. None of these elicited more than mild curiosity. Occasionally a different scent would trickle over the hare's home range, a scent to which he reacted by quietly moving away or by freezing into immobility. Sometimes it was the pungent trace of fox, sometimes the musky scent of weasel. Occasionally it was the sweetish odor of black bear. The scent that caused the hare to run, dodge, and freeze was the unmistakable odor of lynx.

As the year wore on the sun rose and set each day farther to the south, and each day it was visible for a shorter period of time. The nights became true dark periods again. Day by day the air became cooler. The aspen and birch leaves turned golden yellow and began to sail down to the forest floor. The light changed from yellowish green to yellow, and the hare's home range became brighter as the leaves fell and exposed the forest floor to the sky.

As the days shortened the hare had started to change pelage. First the tops of his huge hind feet had turned white, next his ears. Autumn progressed; the white of his belly extended up his sides and a white patch appeared on the back of his head and neck. By October he was mottled grayish-brown and white.

Also by October the moose were in rut. In early morning there was the crash of heavy bodies thrusting through the brush, the grunt and whine of a cow moose and occasionally the whistling bray of a bull as he proclaimed his defended area. One evening near the hare's home range, two bulls locked in a titanic, crashing, clanging struggle. They slammed over young birch and tore the moss with their splayed hoofs. They finally separated but in the dim light of early morning rejoined in battle. After the conflict was over, hares from adjacent home ranges congregated at the site to feast on the tender twigs of the broken and bent small trees. The hares knew not of victor or vanquished, only that a supply of new food was suddenly available.

The first snows sifted down over the taiga. Under the bare birches and aspens the snowflakes fell onto the ground and

47

remained there. Every bent alder trunk had a coating of snow on its upper surface, and a dark snow-free "shadow" beneath it. The sweeping limbs of the spruces caught the falling snow and soon every spruce stood in the center of a snowless dark circle. The total visual effect was to make the hare's home range a mottled pattern of whites, dark greens, browns, and blacks. Into this variegated background the hare's own harlequin coat of brown and white blended nicely. The camouflage was doubly effective because the fox, the lynx, and other mammals that might relish a hare were all color-blind and saw only shades of light and dark.

More snow sifted down, and the dark areas on the home range diminished in number and decreased in size. By November the snow was thick enough to hide logs, fallen branches, and brush piles under a cover of white and to spread a dusting of white over even the qamaniq. By this time the hare was in full winter pelage—pure white except for black ear tips. These black points in conjunction with his large black eyes accentuated the white coat. The hare's behavior changed, and he no longer fled precipitously at the slightest disturbance. Now he would remain crouched into a formless bump while fox or lynx padded through his home range.

With snow for a substratum, the hare's trails, invisible in summer, became evident. The home range was truly a network of trails, from willow clump to spruce cover, from spruce cover to birch clump, from birch clump straight across an open space to willow thicket, and back to spruce cover. On most of his movements to food and cover the hare followed his established trails. As the snow cover built up he was not restricted to his trails as deer would be. Because of his large hind feet with their wide-spreading toes and thick covering of stiff hair he was supported on the snow cover instead of sinking in and floundering helplessly. Thus the hare could travel over the snow and visit willow thickets other than the ones he used extensively.

Now, in early December, the days were short with the sun coming into view on the southern horizon for only a few hours. But it was just below the horizon for several more hours in the morning and afternoon. From about eight until four the day was one continual sunrise and sunset, with the light always changing in intensity and color. It was not only the sky that glowed but the surface of the snow reflected the sky. But to the hare it was all in monochrome.

When early in the morning the light began to increase the hare would stretch and preen his fur. Then he hopped along a trail to a willow thicket. Reaching up, he clipped a twig and demolished it between his grinding cheek teeth. Bark and cambium contained relatively little nutrient, and many twigs were required to satisfy his hunger. Sometimes he would twist his head and chip off mouthfuls of bark and cambium from the willow stems.

As long as fresh snow fell the food supply was plentiful, almost unlimited. Each increment of new snow onto the cover elevated the hare so that he could reach a fresh layer of bark or twigs.

In late December no fresh snow fell for several days, then for a week, then for two weeks. The total thickness of the cover actually decreased somewhat as the cover compacted and settled. In their usual thickets the hares soon ate all the bark and twigs they could reach by standing on their hind legs. Then they began to visit the thickets that they usually avoided because of having to cross open expanses of snow. As the snow-drought continued they were forced to utilize the small solitary birches that were scattered over larger and more open areas. On these open spots they were more easily

49

seen by the horned owls and great gray owls that patrolled the sky on soundless wings. Scarcely a night now passed without the scream of a hare as great curved talons ripped into its guts. These violent deaths were a necessary part of taiga life, since unless the annual crop of hares was reduced to the original number, their population would double, triple, or explode.

After nearly three weeks of drought a few wisps of cirrus appeared high in the sky. The cirrus thickened and was followed by lower clouds. The air temperature rose dramatically; a few flakes of snow spiraled down. The snowfall increased in intensity, and by morning all of the hare's world was an impenetrable, swirling gray opaqueness. The hare remained snuggled in his form at the base of a small spruce. All that day, that night, and the next day the snow sifted down. In late afternoon the snowfall slackened and finally stopped; the clouds thinned. The hare pushed out from under the snow-covered spruce, blinked, and shook himself. The moon was just past full, and as the sky cleared, the moonlight glittered and sparkled in the reflections from fresh snow crystals.

Now the hares had a fresh supply of food because the new snowfall elevated them more than a foot higher than they had been before. Moreover, the willows, alders, and birches were bent down under their loads of snow and the tender topmost twigs were within reach. All the old hard-packed trails had disappeared under the new fluffiness. Only the hare's keen sense of smell and spatial orientation enabled him to follow and re-establish his network of trails.

A sudden urge to run smote him. From one border of his home range to another, back and forth, he leaped, sending up a fluff-cloud of snow crystals every time his great hind feet came down. The urge to run hit all the hares on the hillside, and soon the moonlit taiga was full of darting white shapes, leaping and cavorting, all in mindless silence. This display was not "play" or true social interaction, but a behavioral adaption evolved through millennia of taiga life for the purpose of re-establishing a trail network.

After the snowstorm passed, the air pressure increased as a great dome of cold, dry air moved over the taiga. The temperature slid lower, hour by hour. At night the sky literally sucked the radiant heat from any warm object exposed to it, and the hares were no exception. Since they lived on the snow surface they were exposed not only to the low temperature of the air but also to the infinite heat sink of outer space.

As the deep cold settled over the taiga the twigs grew brittle as glass; the snow squealed under the hoofs of a moose as he crackled through the willow thickets. When the hares fed they crouched with feet drawn underneath their bodies and their ears tucked back snug against their withers. Their fur was fluffed out to provide maximum insulation; it formed a fringe or skirt around them as they crouched feeding.

When the air temperature slid below −50 the hare avoided exposure to the heat sink of the sky. Now he spent long hours crouched in the snow caves under the snow-bent alders and birches. Here he was protected from losing infrared heat to the sky by the radiation shield of snow above him.

The hare returned to his form from a feeding excursion to a willow thicket. As he hopped along his trail beside a clump of snow-bent young spruces, a great crushing weight suddenly pinned him to the packed snow of the trail. His scream of pain was cut off as long teeth crunched through the base of his skull into his brain.

The lynx lifted his head, licked the blood from his lips, and twitched them in a gentle snarl of accomplishment.

The Artist of Ambush

The great glacial river flowed sleekly, looping in great meanders through its taiga-covered flood plain. Only the speed of the flotsam carried along on its surface gave any hint of its repressed power. A whirlpool occasionally dimpled the creamy-tan surface, or the gaunt skeleton of a traveling tree lifted broken arms as it rolled in the current. An undercut section of the river bank collapsed and more debris, already waterworn, streamed down from the raw scar.

The river and its rising and falling was the great pulsing aorta of this entire region. Its springtime rampages, when great ice blocks tumbled, crashed, and squealed, and ice jams backed up water over square miles of forest, were the source of nutrients for unnumbered sloughs, oxbows, and ponds. The floods flushed out pools stagnant since the previous spring. Over the taiga floor they spread a thin layer of rock flour and debris, a layer rich in mineral nutrients that served to circumvent the depauperating effects of the rigorous subarctic environment.

The churning, gouging, undercutting, and deposition by the river built up mudflats, sandbars, and islands. As soon as mud or sand stabilized at a higher level than the water, plants invaded. First there were yellow carpets of bladderwort, followed by masses of purple flowers of willow herb. Then came the willows, first as limber switches, then as dense, nearly impenetrable jungles. The closely ranked stems and trunks slowed subsequent flood currents enough for silt to drop out of suspension. Thus the bars grew into islands.

The writhing river built up and tore down. Always the entire spectrum of bare mud to tall willows to mature spruce taiga was present nearby.

Here congregated the moose, to strip the leaves and tender twigs of willow. Such an array of vegetation types, particularly the willow stands, was heaven on earth to those "low-bush moose," the snowshoe hares. Their trails, outlined by scent, crisscrossed the willow stands, ran straight across the strips of sedges that marked the graves of abandoned river channels, and broke up into looping networks under the mature spruces.

At the edge of the forest, on the high bank overlooking a sedge slough and the willows beyond, in a patch of warm sunlight, lay a mat of fur. One end of the mat resolved into a head that rose up and looked around sleepily, then plopped back onto the warm moss. The head had pricked ears, gray in front and black behind, each with an upstanding tuft of black hairs. Long white vibrissae fringed the face. The eyes whose gaze swept sleepily across the marsh were large, clear, golden, and outgoing. (The man who coined the phrase "lynx-eyed" to indicate a penetrating or searching expression had obviously never looked attentively at a lynx, for a lynx's gaze,

54

although keen, is calm, dispassionate, and self-assured, in fact, almost innocent.)

No mammals can relax so completely and bonelessly as can the larger carnivores, and the lynx lay for some time inert, like an empty skin. Then she roused, stood up, and stretched luxuriously, giving a great tongue-curling yawn. She weighed about thirty pounds but stood on legs so long that her body appeared disproportionately small. The legs ended in great rounded feet, again out of proportion to her size. The paws looked soft and cuddly, but they were equipped with sharp, recurved, and retractable claws. The lynx stretched her body again, flicked her short tail, and stalked away. Although her body parts were all out of proportion to each other, the moment she moved they all slid into the harmony of smoothly controlled power.

The lynx gave a hollow, throaty "meow," sounding for all the world like a domestic tomcat. At the sound the forest exploded with movement. Two smaller copies of the adult lynx bounded toward her. She cantered away on stiffened legs. The kittens immediately accepted the invitation and pounced on her. They all went down in a writhing ball of gray, brown, and white fur. When juvenile exuberance finally went too far, she growled a warning and sat erect, and the kittens cascaded down her flanks. The kittens were young, but had already learned what that growl-tone meant. They stopped their roughhouse and began industriously to lick and clean their feet and legs in a displacement activity.

When the lynx arose and walked off in head-lowered attention, the kittens knew that this attitude, plus the slight twitching of her black-tipped tail, went with the exhilaration of the hunt. They bounced up and followed, fanning out one on each side of the female at about twenty yards' distance. Earlier in the summer, when there were four kittens, the lynx family had been a formidable skirmish line as they swept through the taiga. But one kitten had been snatched away by a great horned owl, while another had run up a spruce trunk overhanging the river, fallen off, and been swept away and drowned.

The lynx, in the exuberance of feeling her muscles flow, bounded ahead and leaped onto a large fallen birch log. The log was a mere shell of tough bark and it resounded under her foot pads. She stretched her forelegs and dug her great scimitar claws into the log. She ripped the claws toward her, lacerating the bark. She bounded along the trunk, gave a great leap ahead, and then sat down and froze. These leaps, triggered by her sense of power and well-being, were deeply ingrained as a part of her being. Pleasurable sensations, they were in fact one of the evolutionary adaptations of the lynx for hunting snowshoe hares, for the sudden bounding movement sometimes caused a camouflaged hare to bolt. At other times the freeze and virtual disappearance of the lynx after the spurt of movement caused a hare's curiosity to overcome its own freezing. Then it might cautiously sit erect and peer in an effort to relocate the disturbance. In either case the hare might reveal itself and the lynx would pounce.

After remaining immobile for several minutes (the kittens had followed the adult's example) the lynx proceeded onward. She shifted her direction to walk through a clump of tall alders and peered into the hollow under their leaning stems. Suddenly, giving a long bound and leaping high into the air, she caught a half-grown spruce grouse that clattered aflight a split second too late. With her forepaws she pinned down the flapping bird and then crushed its head with her teeth.

The kittens descended upon her and snatched the still quivering carcass. They both gripped it with their teeth and tugged and growled at each other. The adult lynx busied herself with licking and cleaning the fur on her forelegs and paws. After the fur was cleaned and rearranged she wiped her face and ears with her paws, then gagged and rubbed her lips to remove a grouse feather still clinging to her mouth. She rose and continued her hunt. The kittens would settle their food-scuffle by themselves and follow her trail later.

The taiga summer passed. Aspen and birch leaves turned golden. The kittens grew until they were almost of adult size, but they were still mostly legs and feet. They were frequently distracted from the serious business of the hunt by the fluttering spirals of falling aspen and birch leaves. One kitten would leap into the air in an attempt to catch a falling leaf; the other would pounce on the first and the youngsters' role in the hunt dissolved into a wild, furry tumbling. The nights grew cool and the dawns became a panorama of pastel orange and yellow. Frost crisped the marsh grasses and sedges, while the horsetails turned yellow. As the sun rose, light streaming between the dark cylinders of the spruces struck the columns of vapor that twisted and curled above the slick black surfaces of ponds and oxbow lakes. The sun now had to climb well up into the sky before the mist-columns evaporated and disappeared.

The shortening of light was translated by lynx hormones into a fresh growth of fur. The lynx appeared to swell and grow heavier as their coats lengthened and turned lighter in color. Stiff hairs elongated on the bottoms and sides of their paws, making them look even larger.

The crisp golden days of the subarctic Indian summer shortened. The swift changes in solar energy allowed the low-pressure areas to push northward and encounter colder air. Rain fell on the taiga. Abscission layers softened, parted, and aspen leaves, now a dull yellow, plopped onto the soggy forest floor.

57

As the lynx family moved through the willow flats they were showered with fine spray. Although they would show no hesitation in plunging into water to swim across it, the constant drip and splash irritated them. The adult particularly was annoyed by getting her ears wet. She would shake her head vigorously, sit down, and attempt to dry them with their long tufts by rubbing her forepaws over them. Finally her placid temperament could stand no more and she retreated to the shelter of a cutbank, where the feather-moss and root mat hung down over the edge like a curtain. Here she licked and cleaned her fur, then tucked her feet under her, and surveyed the dripping world outside. The kittens crowded into the shelter, but when they attempted to rub against her she snarled at them and lifted a forepaw. The kittens retreated to the other end of the shelter and cleaned their own fur. Then they, too, tucked their feet under them and placidly watched the river run by.

As autumn progressed, the wet vegetation froze into a tinkling latticework. Hare-hunting was now virtually impossible, since the lynx's every movement was to an accompaniment of tinkling, crashing, and swishing. For an animal in which silent movement was so much a part of its nature, such a situation was intolerable, even traumatic. Consequently, the lynx family moved as little as possible. They hungered, and were kept from severe hunger only by the fact that the glaze affected voles even more than themselves. Thus the lynx family, even the kittens, caught voles whose warm nests had become infiltrated with freezing rain. Each vole was only a mouthful, but in the aggregate they ensured survival.

Then came the snow! As the api built up, the lynx reveled in it. This was their world. The adult lynx was more prone to engage in a tussle with the kittens, rolling in the fresh snow, and then bounding away with the kittens tumbling after. The

noisy ice-encrusted horsetails were now well hidden and the lynx could slip silently through the willows. As the qali accumulated it deadened the transmission of sound through the forest, causing the lynx's keen sense of hearing to come into full play.

The kittens grew more proficient as hunters. Each had actually caught a hare, but they still had much to learn before they would be able to take care of themselves. The lynx family was, nonetheless, a powerful force as they swept through the willows in skirmish line.

The adult lynx bounded ahead, then froze. Her tufted ears caught the slight sound of a dried willow leaf scraping against a stem. Her head slowly swiveled around and, as her great yellow eyes focused on a dim cave under qali-bent willows, the black pupils expanded. The kittens mimicked the adult and they, too, froze in expectant attitudes. The adult lynx leaped toward the willows; a white hare burst out in a puff of snow crystals and sped away. The lynx bounded after, her long legs carrying her closer to the fleeing hare. The hare dodged, and passed directly in front of one of the kittens who was flanking the adult. The kitten tried to turn, skidded, and tumbled into a willow which dropped its load of qali onto him. The adult leaped over the frantic kitten and gained on the hare. She anticipated the hare's next dodge and pounced with all claws extended. The hare screamed and kicked as the great claws penetrated; then the lynx crushed its skull with her teeth and the hare quivered into death.

As the subarctic winter progressed, the snow sifted down, light and fluffy, in an ever-thickening layer of api. As the fluffiness increased, even as the hares sank in more and more. They began to form trails which, as they compacted, sank several inches below the general snow level. The lynx, even with their great floor-mop feet, were hindered in their movement and they, too, began to use the hares' trails.

The Artist of Ambush

In this white, yielding world the best hunting technique now was ambush. For hours at a time the adult lynx and the kittens crouched motionless in qamaniq under low-sweeping branches. Sometimes two or more days passed and not a hare came by their lairs. Then the lynx family resumed their skirmish-line hunting, but such actions were not efficient because the hares still had quite a flotation advantage. The lynx family caught less than half the hares they chased.

They remained lean. Indeed, leanness was another quality of the lynx; natural selection had molded in them a precise adjustment of body weight and supporting area of paws to snow density. But conversion of body fat is a physiological way of ensuring survival over a food shortage, particularly a food shortage combined with the body stress brought on by cold. Now there came into play an adaptation possessed by several taiga mammals, a mechanical adaptation. Such mammals, instead of being forced to increase their metabolic rate to maintain body temperature, relied on extremely effective insulation. Thus the lynx did not really need body fat; their long, thick fur isolated them from all but the deepest cold. They could go for days or even a week without making a kill, and still suffer no harm.

During this year of the lynx's life there had been frequent snowfalls, so that the api constantly increased in thickness. But now the great Polar High tightened its hold on the taiga, and the air became drier and colder. Molecules of water sublimed from the ice crystals at the top of the api, while at the base of the snow cover pukak formed. Both forces caused a slight shrinkage and subsequent settling of the api.

On the surface, the hares now found that they could no longer reach the fresh bark above their previous feedings, so they moved to adjacent stems for fresh bark. As the snow-drought continued and the api settled still more, the hares were forced to leave their choicest and densest willow stands;

61

they ventured into untouched stands where the willow stems were farther apart, and eventually they scurried across open areas to reach isolated clumps of willows.

The shrinkage of the api compacted its surface and the hares were no longer limited to established trails. Their tracks spattered all over the snow surface. The lynx family began to have more success at hare-catching. The skirmish line swept through the willow stands, across open snow-covered sandbars, up the bluff, and through the mature spruce forest. They even crossed the wide snow-plain of the frozen river, clambering over the slick tumbled ice-boulders of the pressure ridges. On these long excursions each lynx, even the kittens, felt constrained to urinate frequently. They did so every fifty to a hundred yards of their travels. Each orange-yellow stain on the snow surface proclaimed the home range of the lynx family. As the family crisscrossed their home range they traveled about five miles every diel period.

Every drought must end, even a snow-drought. As snowflakes sifted down, thicker and thicker, the lynx took shelter under dense spruces. Well-fed and warm in their snug snow caves they dozed away the hours while their taiga world dissolved into a gray featureless swirl of falling snow.

The air mass that was dumping the snow drifted away, pushed eastward by a dome of dense, cold, and dry air. The atmospheric changes roused the lynx; they pushed up through the fresh snow which blocked entrances to their snow caves and emerged into a world completely new. Nearly a foot of loose, fluffy snow covered the old track-bespattered surface; qali-covered branches bent low and the deepened qamaniq had sheer walls. The night sky was clear, and brilliant moonlight reflected from a multitude of ice crystals—not only on the api surface but on the qali, and even twinkling down through the air. Bright was the moonlight, and the shadows were even blacker by contrast.

The Artist of Ambush

The vertical slits of the lynx's pupils enlarged so that scarcely any yellow was visible. The adult's ear-tufts twitched as she received and sorted the scarcely audible pulse sounds of taiga life—a faint fairy-chime from a boreal owl, a distant chirr from a roused red squirrel, a crackling as a moose thrust through a willow thicket. The lynx also opened wide her mouth and uttered a tremulous far-carrying meow. Then her attention quickened as she caught the vibrations of thumping hare feet.

The skirmish line formed and the lynx family, long legs lifted high at each step, slipped from shadow to shadow. Ahead shone a glittering expanse of open snow. A white form flitted across in the moonlight. The lynx bounded ahead, then changed direction as another hare caught her vision. Then another, and another! The world was suddenly filled with white shapes flitting and flashing in the moonlight. The lynx sat down and stared. Never had she seen anything like this.

Then one of the kittens bounded and pounced on a hare. The hunting instinct triggered the adult's muscles and she, too, leaped and pounced. Even the slower kitten killed a hare.

The mad midnight dance of the hares, triggered by the pleasurable sensations of competitive chases through the fluffy snow, was actually the culmination of complex behavior mechanisms that had evolved in the hare population and which ensured that surplus members were exposed to predation. The lynx family was not alone in catching hares that night. Throughout the entire region other lynx were successful, as were great horned owls, great gray owls, and foxes.

The clearing skies that brought the bright moonlight also brought a spell of the deep cold. Hour by hour heat flowed from the dry, calm air to outer space; the snow surface chilled, as did the willow stems, the spruce trunks, and needles. When the air temperature sank to more than fifty-five degrees below zero, the hares retreated to the snow caves formed by qali-bent alders and willows. At this temperature the air was so cold and dry that it transmitted virtually none of the molecular emanations from living bodies. The lynx walked in an essentially scentless world; their sensory windows onto this world were now their eyes and ears. The lynx had a poor sense of scent anyway, another adaptation to the taiga where so much of the annual cycle is passed in the deep cold, so they were not handicapped as much as was the fox.

By the time the deep cold had passed the kittens were more proficient as hare-hunters. They caught one out of every three or four hares they sighted and chased, a record of success almost equal to the adult's. Concurrent with their independent ability they hunted more on their own accord. Sometimes they prowled separately for a day or more, re-encountering each other only because they still habitually followed the looping routes used by the adult. But no longer did the adult lynx bound in invitation to a chase; no longer did she and the kittens engage in elaborate games of mutual stalk and pounce. Now when the kittens approached she snarled and moved away alone. In the shortening nights her throaty yowl could be heard through the taiga.

One of the kittens, after being rebuffed by the female, curled up in the qamaniq under some small spruces. He dozed for a while, then his yellow eyes opened wide and his black-backed ears twitched. He caught faint crunching sounds on the snow surface. There! A flash of white right beside his ambush! The kitten leaped, and pinned down the white hare under his huge paws. The hare's scream was cut off as the lynx bit his head.

The lynx lifted his head, licked the blood from his lips, and twitched them in a gentle snarl. He reached down to get a firm tooth-hold on the hare, and then walked off with the still quivering carcass. The hare's huge feet trailed alongside, furrowing the snow. The lynx dragged the hare up the bluff to the shelter of the larger spruces, where the snow was hardened by qali-falls.

The lynx nuzzled the hot carcass, then nipped the belly skin with his incisors. He held down the carcass with his feet and gripped the belly with his teeth. He pulled sharply and disemboweled the carcass. He flipped aside the steaming stomach, intestines, and caecum, and lapped the blood in the abdominal cavity. Tipping his head sideways, he engaged his bladelike carnassial teeth around the thoracic wall and cut the weak ribs. Cutting and pulling, he worked his way through the carcass until nothing was left on the spot but the ears and a long scrap of skin. The hare's huge hind feet were inedible (indeed, virtually indestructible) and were also discarded. These scraps, plus the blood that soaked into the packed snow, were all that remained after the lynx's feeding.

Neatly coinciding with the breakup of the lynx family and the youngster's newly acquired independence was the sudden appearance of voles on the snow surface. The scurrying rodents, evicted from their subnivean galleries by the rising concentration of carbon dioxide therein, furnished easy hunting for the still lubberly kittens.

Late one afternoon, as the long shadows pulled through the taiga, one kitten descried, far ahead, a strange harelike shape on the snow. Not a hare's color, it was a dark brown. The kitten, black tail a-twitch, flowed from shadow to shadow as he stalked the creature. There! One ear moved; it must be a hare. The kitten gathered his feet for the final consummatory dash. He sprang, and landed, not on a hare, but on the long-eared head of a young moose, a short yearling, that lay in a deep bed in the snow with only his head protruding.

The young moose gave a bleating snort and swung his head

violently. The kitten was thrown off and thumped against a willow trunk, temporarily stunned.

The kitten dimly heard a blasting squeal and scarcely saw the huge bulk of the cow moose before she reared above him. Then the great sharp-pointed hoofs plunged down, crushing the kitten's ribs and shearing his spine. The aroused cow continued to rear and trample the mangled mat of bloody fur long after life had left it. Finally it ceased to release her attacks and she turned to nuzzle the yearling. Then both moose crashed away through the tangled willows.

The Master Hunters

In the pale blue bowl of the sky the sun traveled on an annular path around the zenith. For a week the sun had not dropped below the horizon and it would not be out of sight for yet another week. The land on which it shone was north of the Arctic Circle—a treeless, rolling land of long parallel ridges and swales. In late June there was still ice on the lakes, and many of the swales and ravines were full of snow. This snow was not the hard wind-carved snow of the tundra winter but remnants of it—a heavy, wet, crystalline stuff that collapsed underfoot.

As the sun's heat reflected from the earth in shimmering waves the variegated pattern of heat-absorbing gravel ridge and heat-reflecting snow bank caused weird mirages. The distant hills floated above the horizon as battlements and crenelated towers, then sank out of sight only to rise again in a new form.

On the crest of a gravel ridge a wolf appeared. Her coat of steel-gray was ragged and worn, with great tufts of the long winter hairs hanging loose. In her jaws she carried the lifeless body of a ground squirrel. As she trotted over the ridge the squirrel's tail flopped loosely, as did the tufts of long winter fur remaining on her lean flanks. The female was emaciated from the metabolic drain of lactation. The ground squirrel's carcass was lean, too, but every bit of meat helped to fill her pups and to lessen their urgent nuzzlings for her milk.

Far ahead of the wolf the pattern of parallel ridge and swale was broken by a higher ridge which traced a sinuous course toward the wavering horizon. This ridge was not gravel but was composed of sand, with steep sides and with smears of twisted dwarf birch and willow in protected niches. Such a ridge is an esker, a legacy of the not so distant days when the great continental ice sheet had scoured the land. The ice sheet had finally stagnated and begun to waste away. Meltwater had poured through a monstrous crevasse in the ice and finally choked the crevasse with churned-up sand. The sinuous deposit of sand, miles long, had become the esker and, because of the easy digging, it provided a den site for the wolf and her mate.

The den had been originally excavated by Arctic foxes but wolves, many generations ago, had pre-empted it. Each breeding season, they had enlarged and modified the original den until now it was a labyrinth of narrow tunnels and entrances. Only a small portion was used each year by the adult wolves but the pups had free range through all the tunnels.

The gray female wolf trotted over the last gravel ridge and abruptly changed her course. She circled far around the den until she was downwind of it and then approached upwind. As she came up to it she gave voice to a throaty, chuckling noise. A chorus of puppy yelps and squeals answered and a mass of fur boiled out of the den entrance. The fur separated into five pups who cavorted toward the female and swarmed around her, tugging at the squirrel in her mouth. She released the squirrel and it was claimed by two of the pups who started worrying the carcass. The remaining pups nuzzled the female's mouth and head, licking and chewing her thick throat fur. She extended her neck and lowered her head. Her sides heaved and she regurgitated the remains of three more ground squirrels.

It had been a successful hunt—the lucky find of a shallow, easily excavated ground squirrel burrow that had yielded not only the young squirrels but an adult as well. Not often did the wolf have this kind of luck. Sometimes she returned to the den empty-mouthed, empty-stomached, or with only a portion of a long-dead caribou fawn carcass. Her mate hunted assiduously, also. He usually cached his contributions some distance from the den—too far for the pups to find it. The female used these caches for her own food.

Her mate had now been absent for two days. The female felt uneasy and restless, for the pups were big enough to try to follow her away from the den and only the most forceful nips sent them yelping back to it. Even so, they usually saw her returning and met her nearly a quarter mile from the den. Her motivation to return to the den site was waning while her restlessness was the waxing of the next phase of the yearly cycle—the urge to travel and hunt with a group, her pups and her mate.

Now the pups had consumed the squirrels, and the combination of full bellies and hot sun took effect. They sprawled out in attitudes which had one thing in common—complete relaxation. The warm sun caused drowsiness in the female and her head dropped lower. Finally she, too, rolled over onto her side and let the sun's heat flow through her.

The pups slept soundly but the female frequently roused, lifted her head for a look around the horizon, and collapsed again. During one such look her eye caught a flash of white on a distant ridge. Instantly she sat up and focused on it. Was it the big white wolf that was her mate, or was it caribou? Caribou does at this time of the year have bleached, worn pelage and from a distance would appear as white animals.

No, the outline and movements were not of caribou but were wolflike. The female rose, stretched, and eased her way around the group of sleeping pups. Once clear of the den site she broke into a trot and went toward the food-cache where the wolf pair usually met.

As the big white male came nearer she could see he was bedraggled and limped slightly. Actually he had nearly lost his life the day before when, swimming a swollen river, he had been rammed by a big block of floating ice and squeezed between it and the river bank. Only a fortunate turn of the ice block and some frantic struggles on his part had enabled him to scramble free. As it was, he had lain immobile for nearly a day until the pain in his leg and side had subsided.

When he approached, his tail went up. The female, seeing this, lowered her head and danced sideways toward him. Then she rolled on her back before him and placed both forepaws onto his shoulders in the traditional greeting ceremony of paired wolves. The two wolves return to the den site, where the white male collapsed, stretched, and slept. Nose on paws, the female lay on the mound above the den and watched.

As the pups grew older the family group became more effective as a hunting unit. Soon the pups were weaned, and without the drain of lactation the female put on weight and her fur became sleek.

Food became plentiful during the tundra summer. Many creatures migrated to the tundra to raise their young. The annual population maximum coincided with the wolves' need for extra food. Lemmings, voles, Arctic hares, caribou—all reached their yearly peak in numbers. The inexorable laws of population mathematics have decreed that all this great surplus must be sacrificed before the next breeding season, all except parental replacements. Thus, lemmings, voles, Arctic hares, and caribou accept the sacrifice of surplus vegetation; Arctic foxes, weasels, and wolves accept the sacrifice of surplus lemmings, voles, Arctic hares, and caribou; while the inescapable bacteria and organisms of decay accept the sacrifice of all and make the circle complete.

This intricate interweaving of relationships that results in the tundra ecosystem is clearly a fragile thing. The annual energy input is quite low. It is parceled among comparatively few species, in contrast to a tropical rain forest, for example. Thus, perturbations within one species population have a far greater effect than would be the case in the tropical forest. Likewise, injury to the system is corrected or healed slowly. Many tundra animals have evolved mechanisms which prevent permanent damage to the ecosystem. The populations of lemmings and voles "crash" regularly, thus preventing overgrazing and permanent damage to their range.

Caribou meet the problem in a different way—they migrate. When the first storms of winter begin to rework and harden the snow cover of the tundra, the caribou migrate to regions of softer snow. As the wolves stay where they can contact caribou, they too perform a geographic migration to the taiga along with the caribou.

For creatures accustomed to the eye-stretching freedom of the tundra, the northern coniferous forest or taiga presented a fearsome situation. The trees towered over the pups, seeming to press upon them, and restricting their field of vision. A whole new world of scents assailed them—spruce gum and birch sap, red squirrel, spruce grouse and moose. And moose! Here was a fearsome creature indeed.

The first encounter one of the pups had with a moose nearly proved his undoing. On an independent exploring trip along a game trail through a frozen muskeg, he crossed a strange scent-drift. He turned and followed it at a run. Suddenly a huge bull moose confronted him with an expanse of palmate antlers, great splayed hoofs, and guttural snorts. The pup made a flying leap to avoid the bull's charge. He had no chance to recover his composure because the bull made a turf-tearing swing and charged again. The pup fled. Only a very skilled or very hungry wolf would face those murderous hoofs without the aid of deep or crusted snow to hinder the movements of such a formidable creature.

Winter closed in. The wolf family group found that hunting food in the subarctic taiga was more difficult than it had been on the Arctic prairies. True, the forest afforded stalking cover, but it also had thick soft snow. Although the caribou travel with ease through snow deep enough to flounder a wolf, they felt constant alarm in the forest. Thus both species reverted as much as they could to something that resembled their ancestral habitat. The caribou rested on open, windswept lakes where the footing and visibility were good. Because the wolves were cursorial beasts, whenever possible they traveled on the lakes, where they, too, had good footing and visibility.

The wolf family, white male leading, trotted single file through the snow onto the lake. As they padded over the wind-hardened snow they came into the view of a band of caribou that were resting on the lake. The caribou, all alert with ear funnels tipped and nostrils wide, stood and faced the wolves. The wolf silhouettes slowly changed shape as the wolves moved across the lake. The caribou relaxed. Several lay down again and resumed the never-ending chore of ruminants—

chewing their cud. No stimulus of danger had been received; digestion could proceed. The wolf silhouettes disappeared into the forest beyond the lake.

For a week the wolf family had used a dense spruce stand as a base of operations. Here they had packed the snow down hard and made trails to all the neighboring lakes. The wolves

had scratched and melted sleeping holes in the snow under the thickest spruce clumps.

One pup awoke. He rose, stretched, and yawned luxuriously. In size he and his sibs were hardly pups. In fact, he was already larger than most sled dogs and his feet were twice the size of a dog's. But in hunting ability, and especially in his knowledge of the intricacies and niceties of wolf social behavior, he was still very much a callow adolescent.

The pup sidled to the big white male and lay down in front of him. The white male opened one eye and rumbled in his throat. The pup thumped his tail. He had learned enough to know this was merely a sleepy greeting. A slightly different tone and timbre would be present in an actual warning. The pup reached out a paw and gently caught the claws in the male's neck-ruff. The male opened his jaws and caught the pup's leg, and his rumbles increased in volume. In ecstasy at this attention, the pup then rolled onto his back, extended his other forepaw and snagged the opposite side of the male's neck-ruff. Without rising, the big male slid closer and transferred his jaw grip from the pup's leg to his neck-ruff. He shook it gently, making fierce rumblings in his throat. The pup suddenly squealed—his neck-ruff was not as thick and protecting as an adult's. The male immediately relaxed his grip, stood, shook himself thoroughly, and stretched. Putting up his nose, he partly opened his mouth and howled softly. Instantly all the pups and the steel-gray female were on their feet. After a confusion of shaking, stretching, nose-touching, and tail-wagging, one by one they gave tentative howls and then all joined chorus.

"Howling" is a poor word to use. "Singing" would be better, except that we have anthropocentric connotations attached to the word. In our language, a male bluebird in his belligerent defense of territory is said to "sing," whereas a wolf in expressing a feeling of well-being can only be said to "howl."

After the singing ceremony the white male leaped completely over the nearest pup and pranced away along the packed trail. All followed. One of the pups turned aside to snuffle at a mouse ventilator shaft in the snow. The female nipped his heel, causing him to leap back onto the trail. They were on more serious business now and after larger game than mice.

As they topped the ridge they could see below them the

white expanse of a large snow-covered lake where several bands of caribou were resting. All the bands were far out on the lake, where the snow was wind-worked and hard; none was near the shore where the snow, protected from wind, lay thick and soft.

The big white male began his stalk. A wolf "stalk" is actually a straightforward sort of thing, not creeping or crawling but simply a slow, steady walk forward. Creeping and bellying are for ambushers such as the lynx; the wolf is a chaser, a runner.

Out onto the lake went the group, plowing through the soft edge-snow. A caribou doe threw up her head and aimed her stimulus-gathering apparatus—eyes, ear funnels, nostrils. The silhouette she received focused across a threshold of stimulation and she threw out one hind leg sideways. Her awkward stance was noted immediately by the remainder of the band and they all turned their sensory windows in the direction she indicated.

The wolves continued their steady advance. The first doe, who clearly had a lower reaction threshold than the others of the band, rose onto her hind legs, turned, and bounded away, then settled into a swinging trot. The remainder of the band exploded after her leaving a trail of flying snow and breath-steam. At the first wheel of the fleeing caribou the wolves broke into a run. The big white male soon slackened his pace, but the pups jostled around him. Long ago he had learned that when caribou fled like that—in a tight group without stragglers—no wolf could overtake them. The pups would have to learn this basic truth for themselves. He resumed his steady trot and was rejoined by the female.

The two adult wolves had crossed the lake and were well up the next ridge before the pups returned, panting and steaming, tongues flapping. As the excess heat flowed away from them, the temperature of their fur slowly dropped again —the frost-line closing in. Each was suddenly clothed in white as the frost-line reached the tips of the long guard hairs and the body-steam crystallized onto them.

The two adult wolves trotted onward, constantly reading the air for the scent of caribou. Each ridge had to be approached and topped in its own way, depending on the flow of air currents. Each caribou trail had to be snuffled and tested for freshness of scent.

Here was real appetitive behavior—a searching, a craving that could be fulfilled only by the consummatory act. For the adult wolves the appetitive stimulus was particularly strong since it was reinforced by the sight and sound of their hungry pups.

The sun was sliding along the southern horizon by the time the wolves came down to another lake. No caribou were on it, because they had already completed their rest and rumination cycle and had returned to the forest to continue their ceaseless search for food. Their scent was still strong in the bowl-shaped resting spots in the snow, and the pellets of excreta were yet unfrozen. The scent of caribou was so strong that one of the pups gave a small squeak of excitement.

The adult wolves broke into a lope and flowed through the fringe of willows at the lake's edge. Ahead, they could see caribou. Again there was the startled focusing of eyes and ears. No need for the alarm pose now, only the upward thrust with the hind legs, the turning and fleeing. One big buck wavered before taking a choice of escape routes. His fleeting moment of hesitation slowed the wheel of fortune and the ball of natural selection dropped into his slot. That moment of hesitation, the difference between immediate response to a stimulus and a slightly delayed response, was all that was needed to release the wolves' chase, the consummatory act.

The Master Hunters

The chase was swift and violent. Caribou and wolves crashed through a willow thicket. The big white male pulled alongside and leaped. He hit the caribou on the shoulder. The great jaws closed on the neck. They twisted. The female and pups hit at the same time. Caribou and wolves went down in a cloud of snow, fur, flailing hoofs, and flashing teeth. The hot smell of blood flowed as a cloud of steam billowed. The caribou kicked feebly and was still. Natural selection has been served.

In the voluminous folklore about wolves there is a recurring theme: "A wolf can catch any animal it chases." We can now understand how this belief has arisen. The wolf can indeed catch any animal it chases; it doesn't really chase any beast unless the chances of success are very high. The probability of success is established very soon after contact—the limp, the slow turn, the delayed escape-reaction; these are the "releasers" that trigger the change from the flexible, searching, appetitive behavior phase to the stereotyped, deadly efficient consummatory phase. If the proper stimuli are not displayed the consummatory act is not released and the searching appetitive behavior continues. The wolves must exhibit or present their "danger-stimulus" complex many times before an appropriate releasing response is obtained. Once it is obtained, success is virtually assured.

When one understands the behavioral sequences leading to a successful hunt, then the biological role of the wolf as a terminal carnivore becomes clearer. The culling function is seen.

Data are available to support this concept. A comparison of two widely separated caribou populations, one "protected" for many years by bounties, poison, and aircraft hunting of wolves, and the other population "protected" for only one year, revealed that the percentage of limping or obviously sick

77

caribou in the more "protected" population was about twice the percentage in the less "protected" population. The genetic and evolutionary implications are obvious. This is the raw material for natural selection.

While crossing a frozen lake one day in midwinter, the wolves' attention was attracted by the sight of black objects against the white snow. They changed course to investigate. As they drew closer they distinguished two small spruce trees protruding above the snow. For any canine, such a thing must be investigated closely.

The scent of caribou hit their nostrils. The adult wolves slid to a stop—caribou scent without any other sign? The incomplete pattern of stimuli caused the big white male to rumble warningly. Three of the pups turned back and rejoined the adults, but the other two dashed on toward the trees. Between the trees they encountered the source of the scent—the hind half of a caribou, buried in the snow. Their hunger and inexperience caused them to forget the formalities of group feeding, and they began tearing and gnawing at the frozen meat.

The adults and other pups circled slowly around the trees, searching the snow for scent. A faint, strange, oily odor caused the big male's hackles to rise, his throaty rumbling changed tone. Another strange scent, faint yet acrid, hit his nostrils. His tail stiffened, his ears went back, and he leaped sideways, then turned and streaked across the snow. The others followed. All except the two pups eating at the carcass. They looked up at the sudden movement, then both gave convulsive grunts as their intercostal muscles hardened in strychnine tetany. They fell stiffly onto their sides. Blood spurted from their severed tongues as their contracting jaw muscles forced their teeth through the flesh. Bodies deprived of oxygen, their eyes bulged. After a few minutes the muscles relaxed and one pup drew a few shallow breaths. Partially revived, he struggled to a half-sitting position. Suddenly his tail threshed wildly, his spine arched as muscles contracted and hardened again. His toes flexed sharply. Suffocation squeezed his life away.

Long after the two wolves died, ravens circled down to the exposed caribou meat. After feeding, they, too, died lingering deaths. One raven staggered into the air and flew half a mile over the forest before fluttering down through the trees. A fox found the raven carcass, devoured it, and died, convulsing, in the snow. A wolverine loped over the lake surface, ate of the poisoned caribou, and jerked through the snow into the forest. The wolverine's amazing resistance to strychnine enabled him to travel for two miles, struggling and snapping at the fire in his stomach, before he too died. From the poison station, pain, death, and destruction spread out over the land like ripples on a pond.

In primeval times the wolf was found all over North America—in the deciduous forests of the eastern seaboard, with the bison herds on the central grasslands, in the mountains and intermontane deserts of the Southwest, in the subarctic taiga and Arctic tundra. The native peoples of North America recognized the wolf as their competitor and the master hunter, and respected him for it. More important, they recognized and cherished the interdependence of all living things. Indeed, the Alaskan Eskimo expressed it as a proverb, "Innuit nelikranya," meaning roughly "Fish eat fish, weasel eat mice, all the same as man." Only recently has such a concept of the ecological community entered the white man's thoughts.

North America was invaded by white men who believed not in the pantheistic philosophy of the interwoven ecological community, but in the Judaic-Christian idea of "dominion

over the beasts of the field." This invasion presaged the doom of many organisms and systems—the sea mink, the eastern deciduous forests, the woodland bison, the plains bison, the wind-resisting prairie sod, the California grizzly, the passenger pigeon. With this invasion the wolf's range began to shrink. At first the destruction of his food supply was more effective than the active efforts against him. The wolf's last stand in the western United States brought forth white man's supreme weapon—poison. Against it no species can survive.

In former days, when intensive food production was vital to our country's economy, the use of poison to protect pioneer cattle herds was perhaps justified. But today, with our ever-growing surpluses of meat and meat products, such efforts to implement meat production only compound a national illness. The more recent adoption of the use of poison in "wildlife management" only reflects the widespread ignorance of biological principles.

Today the master hunter, with the hand of man still against him, is restricted mainly to the North—the tundra and the taiga.

In the taiga the day lengthens, the sun swings higher in the sky, the winter grows stale. The snow, once soft and fluffy, becomes crystalline and crusted. The caribou become restless as it hinders their movements. One day the threshold of sensitivity is reached. A certain level of hardness and density of the snow releases the constrained urge to move, to walk, to follow another's tracks. All through the taiga, caribou begin to move away from the advancing spring. The migration is on.

Within the wolves the gonads ripen. The howling ceremonies take on a new meaning, and a new sound. Now the howling is truly singing. The big white male once again courts the steel-gray female. Their first spring, the pups are full grown but not sexually mature. Family ties are still strong and will remain so until next spring, when the pups will be old enough to strike out alone.

A restlessness afflicts the wolves, too. They become aware of the sharp ablation needles on the snow surface. The caribou trails stretch before them, broad, hard, and inviting. The wolves move along them. The steel-gray female leads, for she has a strong urge to revisit a land of long parallel ridges and swales, a land where the mirages float above the horizon, where the great sand esker twists across the landscape.

Caribou Year

In these same Northwest Territories of Canada, beyond Beverly Lake, lay an extensive upland of long, gravely ridges, interspersed with shallow valleys. No trees grew here; this was the tundra or Barren Grounds, where the wind blew almost constantly. The vegetation on the ridges consisted of mats of a blackish lichen known as *Alectoria*, clumps of hardy sedges and grasses and beds of dwarf Labrador tea in protected spots. It was early June, and there was continuous daylight in this Arctic region. This was Latitude 65° North, about the same as Fairbanks, Alaska, and Cape Mercy on Baffin Island. Winter reluctantly loosened its grip on this land; storm after storm alternated with brief periods of thaw. The temperature ranged from zero to freezing. Snowdrifts formed and reformed as the wind carved them away.

Near the top of a long, sloping hill rested a band of Barren Ground caribou. They were all pregnant does, ready to give birth to their fawns. Instinctively they congregated on these wind-swept ridges, where they could see far downwind and where they could scent any danger from upwind. They fed on the lichens laid bare by the roaring wind. As her turn came to give birth, each moved away from the others a few steps to a spot clear of snow. The fawn was born quickly; there was no time to waste on protracted labor. Only the muskox and the emperor penguin enter the world in a more rigorous environment than the Barren Ground caribou.

The fawn tottered to its feet after only a few minutes. Sometimes the wind bowled it over on the first attempt. It nuzzled along the doe's belly fur until it found the udder; then it suckled the hot, life-maintaining milk. After this effort the fawn collapsed again. The doe also lay down, sheltering the fawn against the wind.

After an interval of an hour or less the doe arose, nuzzled the fawn and lowered her head toward it, down and then up. This action instinctively caused the fawn to get up and follow the doe. On rubbery legs it staggered after her, frequently falling but always getting up and struggling on. Some fawns did not get up; these were soon buried under the drifting snow. The stronger ones tottered after the does, impelled to follow by that peculiar head-bobbing that pulled them on. The doe stopped after a hundred yards or so, allowed the fawn to suckle, and again lay down with it to rest. The procedure of rest, suckle, and totter onward continued hour after hour. Because of this muscular activity the fawn digested the milk, generated heat, and thus lived. If it had not moved and only remained huddled on the snow, the roaring wind would have sucked the life-heat from its body and it would not have survived.

Within a few hours such heroic treatment not only separated the fit from the unfit but strengthened the survivors to the point where they could bumble along at a fast walk after the does. By the next day the fawn kept up with its mother even when she was running.

The doe-fawn pairs attracted others, who congregated to form nursery bands. The nursery bands drifted farther north and always to higher ground, where the thaw had not progressed as far as it had at lower elevations. The tundra snow is beaten by the wind into a hard, rocklike consistency over which the caribou can walk safely. When it starts to thaw, however, they break through the surface. The adult caribou had strength sufficient to fight their way free, but the fawns were too weak to do this. When a fawn became mired in a bank of soft snow it was almost surely doomed, for the doe could do nothing to help. She could only stand and bob her head at it.

The does did not allow strange fawns to approach too close. Each doe had a defended area which moved about with her. If a strange fawn blundered too near, it was met by the doe assuming a characteristic pose—head and neck outthrust, ears laid back, upper lip raised. Even a newborn fawn instinctively interpreted this attitude as threat, and tottered away. If the fawn was not quick enough it received a series of vicious blows from the broad, sharp front hoofs of the doe, or even a quick, puncturing thrust from the antlers.

By late June the vegetation had awakened from winter dormancy; new green growth transformed the whole aspect of the tundra. The fawns now received almost all their nourishment from grazing, and suckled only a few seconds at a time.

Summer arrived with a rush on the tundra. Great flocks of snow and white-fronted geese whistled down onto the melting ponds and lakes. Each tundra pond reverberated with the noise of myriad courting oldsquaw ducks. The Arctic fox cubs tumbled about the entrance to their den, which was dug into the steep side of a sandy esker. The Arctic hares shed their winter coats of silky white fur and were a dull, inconspicuous brown.

One day the nursery band of caribou scattered in confusion before the loping gallop of a foraging Barren Ground grizzly and her two cubs. Although quick and agile, the great blond bear was no match for the swift caribou and their fawns. She continued her forage trip, sniffing for the scent that told of a dead fawn on the tundra. Carrion was more nearly her speed.

In July the sun rode high overhead, scarcely dipping below the northern horizon at midnight. The constant heat brought out the curse of the Arctic—insects. Mosquitoes surrounded the caribou bands in huge clouds. Although annoying, the mosquitoes were no serious problem to the caribou. But when the warbleflies and nose botflies emerged, then life became torment. The warbleflies hit the caribou on their legs, darting in to deposit an egg on the hair. Later these eggs would hatch; the larvae would burrow beneath the skin and then migrate to the back, where they would encapsulate and grow to maturity. The nose botflies hovered around the caribou's head, darting into the nostrils to deposit not an egg but a living larva.

Evolution had provided the caribou with certain protective movements. They stamped their feet, twitched their hides, and placed their heads close to the ground with the nostrils buried in a clump of sedge. Occasionally a band congregated instinctively into a closely packed mass, the "tandara" formation of the reindeer herders of northern Eurasia. In this tight circle only the outer rim of animals was exposed to fly attacks. The exposed animals constantly squirmed their way into the protected center, leaving others to take their turn as a buffer.

Finally some individuals could stand the torment no longer. They started to trot across the tundra, attempting to evade a fly. But this only presented them to other flies and the deluded animals trotted faster and faster. Sometimes one or more went berserk and fled in a labored gallop until exhausted.

The band eventually drifted to a high windswept hill where the flies were less active. More and more caribou congregated on these hills until they were closely packed. Caribou in large aggregations are susceptible to a sort of mass hypnosis. When one animal moves, all move. Sheep and human beings are also afflicted with this tendency. The entire aggregation started to move, picking up other bands and groups as it went. Soon the entire caribou population of the region was congregated into several herds, each numbering thousands of individuals, and all moving at a steady trot. This was "La Foule" or "The Throng," which played so great a role in the lives of the northern Indians. When La Foule swept out of the north, food became plentiful again—not only food but clothing, skin-scrapers, needles, knife handles, and the thousand and one things that were made from caribou. As La Foule passed by, a man could get a winter's supply of meat in one day. Contributing to the ease of hunting was the tendency of the caribou to be less shy when gathered into large bands. They could be taken by arrows and even by spears, especially when swimming the narrows of a lake. If La Foule did not come, starvation stalked the land.

An aggregation of hoofed animals such as this had a marked effect on the countryside. After La Foule had passed, the marshes remained battered into a muddy pulp, and the uplands looked as if a spike-toothed harrow had been worked over them. Literally, no stone was left unturned. The lichens were chopped and trampled, bird nests destroyed, the burrows of lemmings caved in. Generations of caribou had worn deep trails into the tundra. Indeed, the principal migration routes or "deer passes" are identifiable from the air by the parallel trails worn deep into the ground.

In late August insect activity diminished because of early frosts. The frenzied rush slowed. The caribou fanned out over the countryside, feeding avidly. This is the good time of the year for all. Vegetation had completed a summer's growth and was plentiful and nutritious. Berries ripened. The caribou were now close enough to the tree line so that dwarf birch was

plentiful. They fed extensively on it, stripping off the leaves with their mobile lips.

As the bearberry leaves covered the tundra hills with crimson, the bucks put on fat in preparation for the rutting season, when they would feed little. Bucks store fat mainly on the back and rump, where it forms a layer sometimes three inches thick and up to thirty pounds in weight. They completed their new winter coats, with impressive white mane and lateral line.

The migration stopped entirely at the edge of the forest.

Now in September the bucks' antlers were completely formed. In mature bucks the main beams are longer than the animal's height at the shoulders. As growth ceased, the blood supply to the velvet slackened. It started to dry, itching fearfully. The bucks scratched it by rubbing the antlers on small trees. The velvet tore off in long strips, leaving the antlers bloody but hard. Mature antlers are zones of erotic sensation, and the cleaning process accompanies the maturing reproductive drive. By late September the adult bucks were in full breeding condition—polished antlers, dark winter coats with a white lateral line, and heavy, swinging white mane—truly magnificent beasts.

The caribou drifted back onto the tundra again, as the animals instinctively sought open country where the bucks could court the does. The bucks left the bands of does, fawns, and yearlings, and became solitary. Soon they began to run about and threaten each other. The rut was on. They rejoined the females. On sight of a doe a buck would thrust out his head and neck, raise his upper lip, and rush at her. Since this was essentially the same as the threat attitude, the does scattered before him. But when the proper sequence of hormones had acted, and a doe was likewise ready for mating, she ceased to interpret the rush as a threat and did not flee. Now the buck walked about her with a peculiar stiff-legged gait, turning his head from side to side as he displayed his antlers and mane. All these postures formed a definite sequence of events which were mutually exciting to the urge to mate. As in most hoofed animals, copulation was quick. A rush, a single swift thrust, and it was accomplished. As the hormonal level subsided, the does again interpreted the initial rush of the bucks as threat and kept out of their way. Then the rutting fervor subsided.

As November arrived, the winter storms swept out of the

north. The snow swirled in blinding curtains of white. It accumulated downwind of each rock and tussock, the forerunners of the massive drifts of winter. The wind worked and reworked the snow, tossing and jumbling the flakes and grinding them into minute grains and crystals which fit together snugly in a hard, dense cover over the lichen food. The caribou moved, seeking softer snow. They once more traversed timberline, "The Land of the Little Sticks," and entered the forest.

The northern coniferous forest or taiga is an association of plants and animals quite different from the tundra. Here the world gained a new dimension—height. The trees afforded living space for different birds—Canada jays and spruce grouse instead of longspurs and ptarmigan. The red squirrel is a characteristic mammal of the taiga. The trees themselves acted as windbreaks, protecting the snow from disturbance. Thus it lay thick and soft.

The caribou penetrated the taiga until they found suitable snow, not too thick, not too hard, not too dense. In former days, before the white man began his ruthless exploitation of the north, the caribou could move freely, wherever snow conditions herded them. Then the white man, with his constant companion, fire, entered the scene. Year by year, the spruce forest with its ground cover of thick lichens was burned. A few acres this year, a few square miles the next, each year a little more than the last—until today, three hundred years after he entered the North American scene, the white man can contemplate thousands of square miles of scorched and devastated land, covered with scrubby jack pine and popple, the life-giving humus gone, the lichens reduced to a thin crust over the bare bones of the earth. As their food supply dwindled, the caribou population decreased concurrently. From a total of some one and three-quarter million in 1900 to 670,-

ooo in 1954 to 200,000 in 1958, this is the story of the caribou decline. Today there are vast areas where a caribou can find scarcely enough lichen food to keep alive.

In the taiga from November to March the environmental conditions are remarkably stable, so far as caribou are concerned. Clothed in a dense coat of long, hollow hairs which are one of the best animal insulators known, the caribou were virtually unaffected by low temperature. Day after day their lives varied little from a set routine. They rested on the frozen lakes from mid-morning until mid-afternoon, sleeping and chewing their cud. Then, as the winter sun slid along the southern horizon in a blaze of gold, salmon pink and purple, they got up, stretched and moved single file toward the shore. Here the band spread out, each animal sniffing the snow surface. When the strong scent of lichens was encountered, each animal swiftly dug through the snow, lowered its head into the crater thus formed, and pulled out one or two mouthfuls of food. Another few steps, another crater dug, another mouthful of lichens. Over and over this was repeated. If the forest was unburned and the lichen growth was thick and lush, the caribou could get the ten or twelve pounds of lichens it needed by digging only about fifty craters; but if, as is too often the case, the forest was burned fifteen or twenty or thirty years ago, the caribou had to dig several hundred craters in order to get food.

Their hunger satisfied, the caribou drifted back onto the lakes for more rest, sleep, and cud-chewing. Being adapted to the tundra, they felt safer and more secure on the open lake, away from the confining forest. For the next feeding period they moved to the same feeding ground. By now the snow might have hardened, forcing them a bit farther into the forest before feeding. Eventually the band was over the ridge and in sight of the next lake. It was then used as a resting place.

In this band one caribou, an aged doe, was limping. Her right front foot was infected with a fungus, *Actinomyces*. Being unable to dig well, she gleaned a few scraps of lichen from abandoned feeding craters. Her coat was poor and rough, her body thin. She was not actually starving; there was still fat in her bone marrow, but she carried the infection about. With each step a few drops of pus, laden with fungus spores, oozed from the cracked hoof. Healthy caribou coming behind her stepped in her tracks and were infected.

Suddenly a doe threw up her head. She had caught a strange non-caribou movement on shore. As her eyes focused on it, she recognized a characteristic silhouette—the wolves were hunting. She thrust out one hind leg in the pose that all caribou knew meant danger. The silhouette moved; it did not change shape. The wolf was heading for her. She rose on her hind legs, turned and fled in one or two bounds, then settled into the swinging trot that no wolf can match. The rest of the band fled around her, tightly bunched. The loose snow flew up in a cloud, steam rose in the frosty air. The aged doe, limping painfully, fell behind. When the wolves saw this single animal, all their hunting instincts clicked into action and they pursued her. She could not run fast, and was soon overtaken and pulled down. Death was violent but quick. The fungus would infect no more caribou. The wolves fed. When the silhouette of the hunting wolves vanished the band slowed and stopped. They walked a few hundred yards farther, then bedded down again and resumed their cud-chewing.

Several days passed uneventfully. Then, as the band came down to a new lake, they saw some peculiar figures on the snow. Caribou being curious animals, they approached the scene. A short distance from shore two small spruce trees were projecting from the snow. Between the trees was a scene of carnage. Four wolves lay stiff and frozen, their backs arched in death agonies, their tongues lacerated and torn as they had writhed in pain from eating a strychnine-poisoned caribou carcass. Three red foxes were dead, too. One of the foxes had been fed on by ravens. Around this carcass there was a carpet of black feathers where the ravens had died and in turn been fed on by other ravens. Tracks led back onto shore where another fox lay dead. This fox carcass had been devoured by a wolverine, which lay dead nearby. The insidious effects of the strychnine spread out from the original bait, like ripples on a pond, carrying death through the taiga. One of the wolves killed here was the individual that had made the final leap and pulled down the fungus-infected doe.

One evening the caribou were restless; they felt uneasy. The barometric pressure was dropping. The sky clouded over, a whisper of a breeze moved across the lake. The temperature rose. By morning the air was full of swirling snow. For two days the snow fell, the wind blew, and the caribou restricted their feeding activities. As night fell on the second day, the wind slackened and died. The sky cleared and the temperature dropped swiftly. When the morning feeding period arrived the caribou found themselves walking with difficulty through the hardened snow cover. Again they felt the restlessness; the migration urge was awakening. They moved on past their feeding spot, walking single file. As one animal tired it dropped behind and another, fresher animal assumed the lead. For twenty miles they moved in this fashion before the snow cover once more felt soft against their legs. Here they began to feed. This was their new wintering ground. They were now just outside the region where the storm reworked the snow and hardened it.

Thus their movements during the winter were not random or undirected but were governed by the thickness, hardness, and density of the snow cover. Sometimes the softer snow was found only where the forest had been burned, and where lichens were scarce. Then the band had a difficult period, a time when the weaker adults and the fawns were unable to dig many feeding craters and so became progressively thinner and weaker.

One day the band was alerted by strange noises at the other end of the lake—barkings and howlings and strange shouts. A long black line moved onto the lake surface and rushed toward them. No evolutionary mechanism had been provided for this stimulus, no characteristic silhouette released flight as it did in the case of the wolf. The Chipewyan hunter in his toboggan, bouncing along behind his straining dogs, approached the caribou closely before the sled dogs assumed the recognizable silhouette and the band fled. The Indian shot from the bouncing toboggan—inaccurately, of course. One caribou was hit and went down, struggling. Another suddenly grunted as a bullet slammed into the abdomen. This animal ran for half a mile before collapsing. The Chipewyan never found it, for he turned to the animal lying on the lake in full sight. He had lost, through "acculturation," the ancestral law that said all wounded food animals must be pursued until captured. In those days of bows and spears a man had to hunt until he was successful in order to kill enough meat for himself and his family.

The Indian skinned and cleaned the carcass. As he rolled the heart and lungs from the thoracic cavity his knife slipped and cut one of the lungs. The blade sliced through a baseball-sized cyst embedded in the lung tissue. A clear watery fluid spurted out onto the Indian's hand. He did not notice it. After cutting up the caribou he fed the lungs and intestines to the dogs.

The cyst was caused by a tapeworm infection known as *Echinococcus*. The fluid in the cyst was filled with reproductive forms of the tapeworm, each microscopic organism highly resistant to freezing and each highly infectious to man. The Chipewyan eventually was hospitalized for a brain tumor caused by *Echinococcus*. Two of his dogs became infected, and in turn, passed the infection along to the Indian's baby son, who sucked his thumb after crawling over a pile of dog harness which had feces smeared on them.

The caribou which harbored the *Echinococcus* infection had only recently joined the band. If she had been with them when they were pursued by the wolf, she, too, would have fallen behind, for animals with *Echinococcus* cysts in the lungs cannot run far or fast. If the wolves had not been poisoned they probably would have followed the caribou migration to the new wintering area and would have culled the infected animal from the band.

The snow season passed. The caribou moved back and forth through the snow cover, resting on lakes, digging for lichens. Occasionally a storm or warm spell in the region where they were caused the snow to harden and become compacted. Then the restlessness began, followed by the migration until a more comfortable snow cover was encountered.

In late March the days lengthened appreciably. Each day the sun swung higher in the sky, and the caribou felt its warmth. The snow began to fall from the trees; the snow cover crusted and settled. Once more restlessness began, and the caribou moved to find better snow conditions. By April, settling, crusting, and melting swept slowly but inexorably through the taiga, herding the caribou along toward the tree line. The migration picked up momentum. The caribou moved through the dwindling forest, on past the tree line, the "Land of the Little Sticks," and onto the open tundra. The does led the migration.

Onward the band moved, feeding as they went. Onward

past the great lakes the Eskimos call Wholdaia and Dubawnt. In late May they crossed the frozen Thelon River. They pushed on into the extensive upland of long, gravelly ridges beyond Beverly Lake, and reached the fawning grounds at precisely the proper time for the fawns to be born.

The caribou had now completed their annual migration of over a thousand miles. The wheel of life had turned a full cycle. Spring had come again to the Arctic.

Moose Year

As the rotating earth pushed through space, sunlight continually spilled over the part of the sphere previously in shadow. The light flooded the high cirrus clouds with pink and salmon, and suffused the atmosphere with hazy golden yellow. The earth rolled on and the sunlight now struck the trees fringing a small lake. The temperature differential between the frosty autumn air and the relatively warm water caused the lake to steam and its shape was outlined by the mist that rose from it.

Here on the Canadian Shield in north central Saskatchewan the bedrock bones of the earth showed through, scraped clean of flesh by the Pleistocene glacier. The soil that had formed in the relatively short time since the glacier vanished was mostly in basins and depressions between the long gray rocky ridges. Water had collected in many of the depressions, and through time there had occurred the stages of ecological succession from open lake to bog lake, bog mat, shrubs, and finally spruce taiga.

From a patch of tall thick willows near the lake margin came the sound of crackling, breaking branches and a series of low, vibrant, moaning grunts. Then there was silence, broken only by a squawk from a duck hidden out on the lake by the mist, and then came sucking, dripping footsteps. Looming through the mist appeared a large bull moose.

The sunlight struck down through the mist and revealed his great spreading palmate antlers, which were tipped with shining white fingerlike points. From one antler dangled a twisted and broken willow branch. The bull twitched his head and the broken branch dropped off. He confronted another clump of willows, lowered his head and raked his antlers through them, first one side and then the other. Leaves flew as the willow stems crackled and broke. The bull raised his head, laid his antlers back to his withers, and voiced another series of moans. Each moan started high, then suddenly dropped in pitch to a guttural grunt. The bull walked on, stiff-legged, away from the lake, disappearing among the golden-leaved aspens that covered the ridges.

The bull was a relative stranger to this lake and ridge. He had spent the summer a mile away in a hundred-acre burned bog that had grown up thick in willows, aspens, and birch. Now, when the frosty nights of September came, the rutting urge rose within him and he had grown restless. His antlers were hard and polished, his neck had swollen and its skin had grown thick and tough.

The green leaves of summer had gone and moose were now shifting to winter food of twigs and bark. This shift, combined with the hormonal changes that brought on the rut, lessened his hunger drive. The sight of a clump of willows released not a feeding reaction but the desire to push his head through the willows and to feel the resistance they gave to his antlers. The extra pressure thrust on his neck muscles flooded pleasurable sensations through him. These in turn caused him to raise his nose, lift his long upper lip, and give voice to the moaning grunts.

As September passed, the nights grew longer and colder. Ice skimmed the ponds and froze the peaty soil underneath the bright leaf litter. The forest grew lighter as the yellow aspen leaves clattered down, opening the canopy to the pale blue sky. Each morning frost covered the sere grasses and sedges.

The bull whipped through the frosty sedges; his trail through the marsh showed as a dark brown line. Under the aspens his hoofs punched black, sharp-edged hoofprints. The bull was no longer the shy, wary creature of the summer. He was heedless of the noise of his progress.

Even more important than touch and noise was scent. The bull lived in a world of scents; they wreathed and curled around him, drifted with the wind, advanced like a column. On calm nights they were stratified and his hoofs swirled through the heavier layers as if through water.

One damp, cloudy morning he encountered a scent that spun him around upwind to follow it. It flowed along the ridge like a river of compelling urgency. There was a cow moose ahead.

As he followed the scent with his nose elevated the bull groaned and grunted. He came to a deep pool of scent around a spot where the cow had urinated. He, too, urinated here. Then he padded the site with his hoofs until it was churned into a mud puddle. He raked his antlers through the battered peat, rolled and twisted in it. He was thoroughly smeared with mud, and reeked with the scents of urine and of special glandular secretions.

The bull came up to the cow, who fed unconcernedly. He

moved until he was in front of her, standing broadside. He stood motionless as she fed closer and then walked around him. Again he moved, and presented himself before her. As the morning wore on the cow finished feeding and lay down to chew her cud. The bull stood motionless nearby.

In the evening the cow fed again. The scent of her urine stimulated another outburst of digging and wallowing by the bull. After an interlude of grunting and antler-thrashing he swiveled his funnel-like ears to concentrate on a strange sound.

From a distance came a sound of branches breaking, then a bellow—a high-pitched whistling bray that dropped to a series of grunts. The bull moved to put himself between the cow and the approaching clamor. He thrashed his antlers against a small spruce, then raised his head and gave an answering bellow.

Through the forest trotted another bull, heedless of the noise of breaking branches. He trotted to within sight of the first bull. Then he turned and, now stiff-legged, he circled the bull and cow. He tipped his head to one side and back again so that his heavy antlers presented white flashes as the points tipped and bobbed. He stopped and thrashed bushes, groaned and bellowed.

The original bull turned so as to stand sideways to the stranger. He, too, tipped his head and antlers in the ritual gesture of defiance. He thrashed his antlers. He circled the cow and thrust out his nose to sniff her. She did not move away as she had previously done. The bull raised his nose, lifted his upper lip and gave another bellow.

Suddenly he dropped his head and began to feed, pulling twigs through his mouth with short, chopping jerks. The stranger did likewise. Both bulls avoided looking at each other as they moved closer, flank presented to flank.

As if on signal, they turned head to head, antlers lowered.

They slowly moved together, feeling, testing with their antlers. Suddenly the battle opened—antlers clacked and rang as the straining bulls tossed them. The stranger bull was forced back and back, until he broke free, circled, tipped his antlers away and fled.

The noise of his departure faded. The original bull thrashed a shrub and then gave a bellow and grunts of victory. He turned to the cow but she was nowhere in sight. Grunting, he trotted in a circle, picked up her scent and followed it.

As he came up to her, she was walking slowly, occasionally feeding. He followed closely, nose outstretched. The touch of his muzzle caused her to stop. He mounted, he thrust, and the cow slipped from under him, all within five seconds. The cow turned and nuzzled him. Three times during the evening they mated. When the cow chewed her cud and then slept, the bull stood nearby in the pose of courtship display.

All the next day the bull and cow remained together. Once a younger bull came near and bellowed. The big bull thrashed his antlers in a shrub; he bellowed, and the younger bull fled precipitously.

As the sun dropped toward the next ridge the cow, followed closely by the bull, approached a burned area where the ground was littered and crisscrossed with fallen trunks. From this spot, where the visibility was good, came the sounds of rutting moose—antlers whacked on trees, branches broke, grunts and thuds were heard. The clamor stimulated the bull to contribute something. He was answered by a whistling, braying bellow.

Immediately the bull trotted past the cow toward the source of the sound. The ritual preliminaries were telescoped into a few antler-thrashes and the indispensable parallel sidling. The two bulls turned and locked antlers. One was forced back for a time, then the other. Antlers vibrated as they impacted;

saplings three and four inches thick snapped as hulking bodies slammed over them. The bulls paused to rest, their antlers still engaged. The resident bull sighted a movement near one side of the clearing. He disengaged his antlers and, with a squeal, dashed at a young bull who had ventured close and who was sniffing a cow while the patriarch was off fighting. The young bull fled and the patriarch trotted imperiously around his three cows.

He vigorously raked his antlers through a clump of young birch, then knelt and plowed them, one side and then the other, through the leaf litter. He rose, turned and charged his original fighting partner, who was awaiting him with lowered antlers.

Once more they strained and twisted, seeking an advantage. They were evenly matched in size and weight, but the bull with three cows was much older than the trespasser with only one. They broke free and stood side by side. Each began to feed, swiftly ripping twigs from birches and willows. Such feeding was ritualized displacement activity, the result of internal conflicts between the motivations to flee and to fight. They slowly circled away from each other, feeding all the while. When fairly far apart each gave a bellow and then moved to his cow. But there were only two cows remaining. The one that came with the invader bull, and one of the patriarch's, had slipped away. Neither bull would get out of sight of the remaining cows and his rival, so there they stood on opposite sides of the cows.

When the cows lay down to chew their cud and to sleep the bulls remained there motionless. In the dim light before the next dawn, when the white-boled birches were just barely visible, the younger bull began to move restlessly. He first pawed the earth gently, then vigorously. As his rival's white-tipped antlers became visible he began to rake his own through a shrub. The patriarch now stirred and did likewise. The younger bull voiced a bellow, then charged the patriarch who turned to meet the challenge. They slammed together with a ringing crash.

Suddenly the patriarch's hind legs slipped and he twisted sideways. The young bull's right antler gored into his flank. The patriarch grunted and turned away, dipping his head and antlers away from his rival. The young bull immediately stripped a mouthful of dry willow leaves. The old bull trotted out of sight; at every step, partly digested food squirted from the antler-puncture in his flank. Infection would soon flame through his abdomen. He was doomed.

The victor raked his antlers through the bushes, pawed the earth and gave a bellow. Then he walked slowly to the cows, who fed unconcernedly. He moved in front of them and stood in the courtship display.

One cow came into heat and the bull turned his full attention to her, but while he was engrossed in courting her the other cow wandered off. After the remaining cow had been bred and her attraction waned the bull drifted away. As September passed he no longer found any magnetic rivers of cow scent flowing along the ridges. A clump of willows did not release the thrashing urge now; they were once more something edible.

By the middle of October snow had fallen. The bull spent more of his time in the swales and bogs between the rocky ridges. As he once more began to feed regularly he regained the weight he had lost during the rut and his coat became glossy. The fur lengthened and the individual hairs stood more erect from the skin.

Several bulls, now tolerant of each other's presence, formed a loose aggregation. Actually they were together more because of food supplies than because of any desire for company. They fed on willow twigs in the thickets around the borders of the muskegs; on young birch in areas recovering from forest fires.

One morning as the bull crossed an expanse of muskeg to the willows opposite, he heard a branch crack behind him. He spun around and confronted a young wolf, loping along his trail. The bull's ears went back, his head went down and the long hairs along his neck stood up in a bristly mane. He cleared his nostrils with a mighty snort and charged, lashing out with his front hoofs. The wolf agilely dodged aside. The bull checked his charge and turned, digging up the frozen turf with his hoofs. He charged again, and the young wolf fled. Only a very skilled or very hungry wolf would face those murderous hoofs without the aid of deep or crusted snow to hinder the movements of such a formidable creature.

The bull snorted a few more times and the hairs of his mane slowly settled into place again. He continued his leisurely pace toward the willow thickets. The wolf's image faded from his consciousness. Memory in ungulates is mercifully short.

The days grew shorter. Each morning the sun rose farther to the south, stayed closer to the southern horizon and set farther to the south than it had the previous day. Day after day the sky was clear, the air dry and cold, the snow cover fluffy and light. The periods of clear and cold weather were interrupted by intervals when relatively warm, moist air poured over the taiga. The sky was then a thick mass of clouds, while snow sifted down. At these times of dim light the snow-laden spruces loomed through the swirling snow and their tips disappeared into it. The alders bent more and more under their loads of snow; the young spruces were virtually covered. The snow cover built up to eighteen inches, to twenty, and then to twenty-three inches.

The loose aggregation of bulls now spent more time in the uplands. Here, where deciduous aspen and birch predominated, the snow cover lay smooth and even. The young birches and willows were bent over so that the moose could easily clip the tender twigs. Sometimes they reached far overhead, even stood on their hind legs, and pulled down larger birches to get the tender topmost twigs. The trunks, brittle with cold, usually cracked and remained bent down. The twigs and bark of the upper branches were thus brought within reach of the snowshoe hares which shared the habitat with the moose.

In late December, at about the time of the shortest days, the bull's neck muscles began to ache. Frequently he rested his head and antlers against the trunk of a spruce. Once when he pushed, one antler dropped off into the snow. With his head unbalanced he walked on, swinging his head and pushing the other antler into bushes and against trees. Half a mile farther on, the remaining antler popped off. The bull shook himself and gave a few stiff-legged hops. His neck no longer hurt. On his head were two white spots of bare bone. The cells in the skin surrounding them were even now dividing, growing, to cover the bare spots. Soon the new growth of bone would start, the skin would cover it and form the protective and nutritive velvet.

As the days began to lengthen in January the air became drier and the cold more intense. The sun still contributed only a negligible amount of heat to the dense, dry subarctic air. The heat that flowed from the upper layers of the snow cover, the trees, the moose, and the hares was sucked away into the vast heat-sink of the sky where it was lost to outer space. The temperature slowly dropped to -40, to -44, and then hung at -49 for a day. An aspen trunk split and cracked like a rifle shot. The temperature finally slid to -54, where it stayed. The air was filled with twinkling points of light as frost crystals precipitated from the dry air. On either side of the sun shone parhelia, the sundogs caused by refraction of the sun's light by the suspended frost crystals.

The bull's fur was fluffed out so as to increase its insulative value. The moisture vapor diffusing from his skin precipitated as frost crystals on the tip of each hair and he became a silvery-gray ghost. This ghost did not move silently, however, for the snow squeaked and crunched under his hoofs. Brittle, cold-soaked branches crackled and broke at his touch when he moved, feeding, through a willow thicket.

His breath condensed into a cloud of ice fog which hung around him, then drifted slowly down the slope as the colder and denser air flowed into the valley. The bull crackled on through the willows, leaving behind him suspended smudges of ice fog.

During this time of the deep cold the snowshoe hares remained in their snow caves under the loaded alders. Here they were protected from the extreme heat loss to the radiation sink of the sky. The red squirrels had long since retreated to their subnivean nests. Creatures even as large as the fox burrowed and curled within the protecting snow blanket to escape the deep cold. Only the moose, the caribou, the wolf, and the raven were active.

After five days the deep cold relaxed its grip somewhat, then later squeezed down again. For an entire month the taiga was never far out of its grip. Finally, in February, the intense air pressure eased. Wisps of cirrus appeared far overhead. They coalesced into a thin gauzy sheet, scarcely coloring the sky. But the thin layer of moisture reflected heat back to earth and the temperature crept upward in the taiga. The deep cold was broken.

The cirrus thickened to stratus and the air became more

moist. The snow surface, twigs, spruce needles, and tree trunks were still in the grip of the deep cold, however, and when the warmer air flowed around them its water vapor precipitated onto them to form long feathery frost crystals. Soon the forest was in silver clothes. Snow fell, but the air had little moisture remaining in it and the increment was light.

By late February the sun came flooding back. Every day it soared higher, rose earlier and set later. Warmth could now be felt from it. Because of the alternations of warm days and cold nights the surface layer of snow crystals transformed into first a coherent layer and later a tough suncrust.

For every step that the bull now took he was forced to push his long legs through the crust. As the crust became tougher it began to scrape the hairs from the bull's lower legs. Ultimately it became tough enough to support on its surface many of the lighter taiga creatures. The lynx, fox, red squirrel, and hare now padded over the surface of the snow without breaking through.

The abrasion of his lower legs caused discomfort, and the bull reacted by moving. Within a remarkably short distance, about three miles, he found fluffy snow again and once more settled down to his sedentary life. His new range was in a region where good moose habitat happened to lie on north-facing slopes where the noon sun did not strike the snow surface.

Spring advanced through the taiga. The Polar High was forced back by the invasion of warm moist air even into this heartland of the continent. Brisk winds swept through the forest. Snow tumbled from the spruces and jack pines and thudded onto the tough crust below. The aspen trunks soaked up the solar heat and re-radiated it, subliming a cylindrical hollow in the snow around each trunk. On the ridges the gray rock bones of the earth also soaked up the sun's heat and melted free. Along the base of the south-facing slopes pussy willows popped out. The Canada jays began to warble softly in the spruces, and at night owls hooted hollowly in courtship display.

Inexorably, day by day, the sun grew warmer. Now, during the day, thawing occurred, but at night the softened surface of the snow froze and hardened again. At this time the bull scarcely moved from his willow thicket because the frozen snow shattered with sharp edges which actually cut the skin. When he did have to move outside his small trampled yard, he left a trail of blood-rimmed leg holes in the snow.

Soon the sun was so high and the air so warmed that there was no longer freezing at night. The snow cover softened and shrank. Water trickled down the slopes over the spots bare of snow. Water flooded onto the river ice. The dying snow cover now offered no resistance to the bull's movements, but everywhere he moved he splashed water.

One day, when only a few patches of snow remained on the north sides of dense spruce stands, the bull felt the ground quiver under his hoofs and a dull roar pulsated on the spring air. The river was breaking up.

The bull nibbled experimentally on all sorts of plants exposed by the melting snow. As soon as the birch and willow buds swelled, the bull gorged on the new growth. The fresh plant food upset the balance of the protozoan populations inhabiting the bull's rumen, and he rumbled and belched as he chewed his cud.

The new antlers were already longer than his ears, and they soon flattened to form palms. They were covered with tender skin and soft, short fur. The bull moved cautiously to avoid hitting them on branches.

One day the bull was startled by a crashing in a thicket. Out charged a cow moose, head down, ears back, mane bristling. This was the time of calving, and the cow had a pair of newborn calves hidden in the thicket. She allowed no creature to approach them. The bull dropped his ears and fled.

By June the mosquitoes hung around the bull in clouds. His eyes dripped tears and his ears flapped constantly. The sun now stood high in the sky at noon and the heat pressed down. During the hottest part of the day the bull took refuge in a seepage pond in an alder swamp. Here he lay and rolled until he was plastered with thick, black peaty mud. The water cooled him while the mud protected his skin from the blackflies which had now emerged. For all taiga animals, blackflies are a greater torment than mosquitoes.

July was a mass of green vegetation, growing feverishly in the short subarctic summer. The nights were already getting longer, the first harbingers of autumn. The bull grew sleek and fat. His antlers were now almost fully formed. In another month they would be mature and hard. Then willows would once more be for thrashing instead of eating.

People of the Moose

The shadow of night, spreading westward and northward, advanced across the continent. The last light spilled over the earth's shoulder and illuminated the north face of the Alaska Range. The snow peaks glittered in the nearly horizontal rays of the setting sun. Far to the southeast the peaks were already bathed in pinkish alpenglow. To the south and southwest the color brightened to salmon, then to yellow, and finally the westernmost peaks reflected the light in bluish-white.

North of the great range of snow peaks spread the valley of the Tanana River. To the west it was broad and flat, scarred by the sloughs, meanders, and oxbows of the silt-laden river, but to the east the valley narrowed between rolling hills. On the river flood plain uncounted lakes and ponds twinkled in the fading light.

The main tributaries of the river, those that headed high in the mountains, were colored light tan from the heavy load of silt and rock flour they carried. These tributaries received their water from the glaciers which creaked and scoured their way down the mountain valleys, each glacier slowly chipping away the mighty range.

The tributaries that headed in the foothills were not silt-laden but clear and sparkling. Instead of flowing through braided channels over wide expanses of sandbars, these clear tributaries were contained within high banks where the spruce forest grew right up to the edge. Indeed, as the banks eroded, trees tipped and eventually fell into the water.

At one point a clear stream flowed over a large gravel bar. In the water just below the bar there was a peculiar structure —a series of posts driven vertically into the stream bottom to form a V-shaped row. The posts were tied together by a wickerwork of willow shoots. At the point of the V there was a cylindrical wickerwork basket.

On the bank above the fish weir was a small clearing in the taiga. Here were two small houses, each about ten by twenty feet in size, made of poles and shingled with plates of birch bark. The space along one side of each ridgepole was without bark and from these openings drifted a plume of wood smoke. Most of the clearing was covered with a latticework of A-frame poles with horizontal poles between. These were racks for drying fish.

But now, in late June, the racks were empty. The cylindrical basket trap on the fish weir was also empty except for a few grayling that had blundered into it. The racks should have been groaning under a load of split whitefish and salmon, drying in the sun.

Here, by the fish weir, was the seasonal home of four families of Dinje, or the People of the Moose as they called themselves.

People of the Moose

The Moose People were Athapaskans, and like other members of this great family of northern Indians, they were rather small in stature, with delicate facial features but relatively massive jaws. They had small, almost dainty, hands and feet. Their hair was glossy black and their skin was a dusky copper hue. Such a delicate, fragile appearance was deceiving; they were sinewy and tough, able to run all day on snowshoes or sleep even though exposed to cold rain or snow. For generation after generation the rigorous conditions of the taiga had directed the evolution of the Moose People until their every characteristic meshed with the environment to form a well-adapted organism. Their small size, plus their skillful technique of making snowshoes, made them like the snowshoe hare, able to run over the surface of the subarctic snow without sinking in. Their massive jaw muscles enabled them to consume the last tough bits of meat and connective tissue on the bone. Their sinewy endurance enabled them to pursue the mighty moose and literally to run it to death. Over the millennia of taiga life they had evolved an intricate seasonal succession of activities—they fished when fishing was good, hunted moose, mountain sheep, caribou, marmot, each in its period of abundance and availability, and gathered berries when each species ripened in a certain locality.

By late June, the time of hunger was at hand. The caches of meat from winter moose-hunting had been depleted. A late snowstorm had caused the spring caribou migration to swing wide of this region. Usually by the time the first of the summer's mosquito hordes hatched, the Moose People were feasting on fresh whitefish and salmon. But the silvery flood of migrating fish had not yet arrived.

Finally the fish came. They dimpled the surface, then splashed and finally roiled the water below the weir as they fought against its willow withes. The cylinder trap was lifted by four strong men and emptied on the shore. In the short intervals between emptying and replacing, enough fish escaped upstream to reproduce their kind in plenty for future years.

The women worked feverishly at splitting the fish and hanging them on the drying racks. Soon the air was redolent with the smell of fish. Several men lit smudges under the racks, not only to keep away the flies but also to hasten the drying process. Fires burned to heat the rocks that boiled the water in the great bark kettles. The curly-tailed Athapaskan moose-hunting dogs glutted themselves on fish entrails and scraps; then they collapsed in the sun to sleep. Human beings likewise ate fresh fish and then slept in the sun. Life was good.

In a few short weeks the fish run was over and the trap again was empty. Under the hot summer sun the fish on the racks dried swiftly. The underground fish caches were cleaned out and repaired. Fish caches were pits some two by three feet square by three feet deep, with floor and sides of poles. When the fish were dry enough to keep they were packed into the caches and a lid of poles was fitted on. Then on top were placed the heavy bear-proof logs, and finally a thick layer of earth covered all. The fish were now resting on permafrost below and protected above from the summer heat by the thick layer of wood and earth. By wintertime perhaps the fish might be a bit "high," but at thirty below who worried about that.

The end of the fishing season signaled the beginning of the time of summer hunting. Now the Moose People came into their own, for there were none who knew better the trails used by the cows, or the thicket where a great bull dozed.

Along the moose trails the Dinje placed their snares. Each snare, fashioned from carefully braided babiche, was cleverly hidden so that a moose of the desired size would unwittingly thrust his head into it. When alarmed by the light pressure on

116

his neck, he would throw up his head and the snare would tighten. No snare that the Dinje could make would hold a thoroughly alarmed adult moose for long, but this mattered little. Soon the sound of a moose's struggle brought a hunter on the run from his vantage point near several snares. His bow twanged and a flint-tipped arrow pierced the moose's chest.

The sharp, serrated blade of the flint knife sliced through the moose skin. The hunter gutted the moose and began to skin it. Soon another Dinje trotted through the forest. This was the first hunter's *kla*. The Moose People had long ago learned that in the taiga a man cannot stand alone. Not only does he need a wife to care for the home but he also needs another strong hunter to help in the chase. Thus arose the custom of the *kla* or partner. Partners aided each other in the hunt; their wives shared the necessary work of tanning, sewing, and other home duties. Frequently the partners would separate in order to hunt different regions. But each knew that if the luck of the chase were bad his kla was probably successful. When two were hunting together, the killer of the game, by custom, gave his kla more of the prize than he took himself. Thus there was developed a feeling of mutual gratitude and appreciation which strengthened the bonds of the kla system.

As the moose harvest declined in the valley of the fish camp, the hunter and his kla decided to begin their summer migration. The partners, with their families, each went a different way. Long familiarity with the region and with the habits of the animals therein enabled each of the partners to know approximately where the other would be at any given time. Each family moved from moose kill to moose kill, drying and caching the meat and skins not needed for immediate use. Thus each family had a series of food caches throughout their home range. During times of poor hunting they would revisit the sites and obtain rations.

During the summer moose hunting the hunter and his family lived in a series of lean-tos, easily constructed and just as easily abandoned. When the hunter made a kill he cleaned and dressed the moose carcass, then returned to the camp. His wife gathered the bedding skins, the birchbark kettles, the tools and her sewing materials, loaded them on her back and moved the camp to the food supply. The hunter returned to his never-ending routine—hunting, hunting, hunting.

This was the season for still-hunting the moose. All the hunter's skills were brought to bear on finding a fresh moose track, reading the sex and age from it, and then deciding the route of the beast. He traveled silently, making great loops downwind, away from the trail, and then returning to the track. Finally there was no fresh track; then he knew the moose was within the half circle he had just outlined. He silently traversed this area, again in loops, downwind, across, and then upwind. There! In that alder thicket—a dark mass, two huge ears flapping at the mosquitoes. Now he moved even slower, imperceptibly nearer, nearer. The range was now perfect, the moose was unaware. The hunter sang softly his private song asking the moose's pardon for what was about to happen. Even this hunting song fitted the occasion. The tones and timbre did not generate alarm, only curiosity. The huge bulk heaved to its feet and the great ears funneled to pick up the strangely pleasing sound. The bow twanged and the moose leaped. The sharp flint blade entered, but the moose still did not flee. Similar skin pricks from branches were commonplace. The hunter remained motionless, still singing his medicine song. The moose, suddenly feeling sleepy, lowered her head. The deadly flint blade had clipped a major artery deep within her chest. The moose lay down, and then rolled over on her side. The hunter continued to sing for many minutes. The song ended; he came up to the moose and touched her eye with the tip of his bow. No response, the moose was dead.

After the kill the hunter did not move his camp to this moose, but because the camp was just a few hills away, he skinned out the carcass, dismembered it, and struggled home, taking several trips to bring in all of it. Almost none went to waste—the meat was cut from bones and dried; the bones were boiled and cracked and the rich marrow was extracted; the leafy abdominal fat was carefully packed in birchbark vessels and stored for winter; the bones of the lower limbs were saved and made into skin-scrapers for later barter; the lower jaw and molariform teeth were fashioned into a crude but usable saw.

The huge, heavy skin was carefully scraped and dried. Later it would be worked, rescraped, and finally smoked over a slow smudge to give a remarkably light, tough, and useful leather. Each portion of the skin, according to its thickness and suppleness, had a specific use. Even the skin from the ears, tanned with the fur on, was destined to become warm caps for winter use.

With a bounteous supply of food the Dinje family waxed sleek. Almost continously there was a slab of meat roasting by the fire. The first part of the moose to be consumed was the head. It hung, rotating from a twisted length of babiche, over the coals. The muscle fibers of the prehensile lips, and of the pendulous nose, were choice delicacies. The huge tongue, fine-grained and sweet, was cooked by boiling in a bark kettle into which hot stones were dropped.

As the summer waned and the nights became dusky, then dark, the Moose People moved south, closer to the mountains. The forest thinned; more dwarf birch appeared among the spruces. Soon the great buttressed shoulders of the mountains loomed on either side. The time to hunt the white sheep had arrived.

Partners rejoined at traditional camp sites. The women talked and gossiped as they made new moccasins with extra-heavy soles. The children tumbled on the thick carpets of moss and lichen. The hunters repaired their gear, braided new snares, and sometimes went on scouting trips to the sheep country above them.

When several bands of sheep had been located, the hunters went into action. They climbed carefully on a long circuitous route that took them far around the sheep and then directly above them. Here the hunters spread out along the mountainside. Experience told them the probable routes the sheep would take when fleeing up the mountain, away from the women who would later approach from directly below. Along the escape routes, among the tumbled boulders, they set their snares. In those places unsuitable for snares were the hunters themselves. Each had his bow, a supply of flint-tipped arrows, and several spears. The waiting began.

Far below, the hunters could see their camp. The shadow of the mountain crept closer to the camp. When the shadow touched the camp the hunters became alert. They fairly quivered in anticipation.

Rocks rattled below the hunters. There! A flash of white. Then another. Soon the sheep streamed into view, running easily up the steep slope. In the lead bounced a two-month-old lamb, followed by the ewe. Most of this band were ewes and lambs, with a few yearlings and two-year-old rams. One ewe was caught in a snare, and as she fell and struggled the following sheep swerved aside. An arrow flew and hit. The sheep fell and rolled. For a few moments more arrows flew. Then the hunters leaped out and began the job of killing the snared animals with spears. The slaughter was soon over. Fourteen sheep lay dead, meat and skins sufficient to keep the women busy.

The sheep carcasses were light enough so that each man could carry one. Soon a procession of hunters made their way down the mountain back to camp.

The community sheep hunts continued until snow dusted the rocks of the alpine regions. The rocks became slick and the moose-hide moccasins of the Dinje offered no grip on them. Mountain travel became hazardous. Moreover, it was time to prepare for the subarctic winter ahead. The Moose People hoisted their bundles of dried meat and sheep skins and moved back down into the taiga again.

Now, in the moon called *nadil-be-sa*, or the Moon When the Animals Gain Their Winter Coats, the maplelike leaves of the mooseberry plants were russet-red against the yellow horsetails. Birches and aspens glowed brilliant yellow and orange against the spruces. In the flat marshes the sedges became sere and brown, outlining the black bog pools. Every morning streamers of fog curled through the valleys.

Fall was a difficult season of the year for the Moose People. Winter was their joy—then their skill on snowshoes made them lords of the taiga. But fall, with its fluctuating temperature, the streams and lakes with ice too thick for canoes but not thick enough to walk on, with rain and wet snow to soak their moose-hide moccasins and clothing, all conspired to immobilize the hunters. Thus, until real subarctic winter settled settled over the taiga, the Moose People avoided long travel and built themselves snug houses of poles and moss. The hunter and his kla again joined forces, this time to construct a double house for their families.

The fall house was similar in shape to the bark fishing camp, but built of sturdier poles and logs. Blocks of feather-moss, cut from the taiga floor, made the walls and roof thick and warm. When the fire was built in the hearth inside, all the house began to steam. For a few days the house was uncomfortably damp, then suddenly the moss walls and roof were dried out and the interior became snug and dry.

While the autumn rains pattered down and plastered the birch leaves onto the sodden taiga floor, while the early snows whispered through the trees and outlined the dark zhe-quinzee under each spruce, now the Moose People were busy inside their homes. The women made winter clothing—trousers with moccasins and leggings attached, coats of caribou skin, socks of rabbit skin, blankets knotted out of long strips of rabbit skin. The men carved new snowshoe frames, then passed the frames to the women for the intricate task of netting the hexagonal mesh of fine babiche.

Now the moon called nitcun-sa, or the Moon When the Bull Moose Ruts, was nearly over. Snow lay over the forest and the air grew dry and calm. Soon the caribou would appear in the country and the Dinje would hunt again.

The men were now gone for days at a time, off repairing the miles-long drift fences of poles that would funnel the migrating caribou into more restricted spots. Then, one day the cry of "Et-then, et-then!" was passed from hunter to hunter. The caribou came.

First came the does, fawns, and yearlings, picking their way along their age-old migration trails. Those that encountered a fence turned and drifted along it. They were not hurried and the Dinje were careful not to frighten them. Finally the caribou, unbeknown to themselves, entered between the wings of a pound. There was no way out of the pound save through the gaps in the fence, and each gap was filled with a succession of snares and watched over by hidden hunters. When the snares at a gap were all tight around the struggling caribou the hunters loosed their arrows and then went to work with spears.

By early December the sun scarcely rose above the snow peaks to the south. The low-hanging sun cast the shadows of the snow peaks up into the gold and violet sky. When the mountains "rode into the air," the Dinje knew that the time had come for *Tcitciun,* or the winter festival.

The people now abandoned their moss houses and gathered into a village. Here each family made its first winter house—a hemispherical framework of poles covered with furry moose hide, and heaped around outside with an insulating layer of snow. The floor was of spruce twigs, redolent and tangy. In the center of each house was a hearth and above the hearth was the smokehole in the roof. The air within the winter house remained clean and fresh because the great temperature differential between inside and outside caused fresh air to be constantly drawn in through the snow.

The Moose People began the festival of *Tcitciun* with a round of storytelling. All during the twenty-hour nights they would sit entranced, adults and children alike, while an old man would recount the people's history, of the great days when the god-man Tsa-o-sha lived among them, of the hunter who wrestled and killed the grizzly bear and brought its meat to the hungry people.

Each night the people gathered in a different house and each night the children learned more of their heritage. They learned why the grizzly was respected, why the otter was never killed, and why the shrew was to be feared above all else. They learned to forecast the weather by the loon's wail and to interpret the raven's shout when a moose was in his view. The stories and dicta were the strands of culture and heritage that bound the people into a complete entity. After a complete recital of history, manners, and morals of the Dinje, the people devoted two days to *Tcitciun* or the Hook Game. The hunter and his family sat in their house. Suddenly the caribou skin door was thrust aside and a long stick poked in. Suspended from the stick was a length of babiche onto which was tied a wooden hook. The hunter shouted a man's name— no response. Another name—no response. Finally he shouted the correct name and the hook jiggled. Next he shouted the name of an object—dried moose meat—no response. Flaked flint adz? No response. Basket of lingenberries? The hook jiggled. The basket was put on the hook and it disappeared out the door.

All through the day the hunter and his family, laughing uproariously, gave whatever the hooks wanted, until by nightfall they had virtually no possessions left. Next day was their clan's turn to visit and dangle the hook. When they finally returned home they again possessed a complete array of tools, clothing, and food, some new, some old, but all *gifts*. Thus, just as the gift custom bound the hunter to his kla with bonds of gratitude, so *Tcitciun* bound all Moose People together. No matter how far apart they might travel, each Dinje knew that he was a brother to all other Dinje with whom he had played the Hook Game.

Other games followed, and the twenty-hour nights were filled with stories. All gossip and news of the past year was retold. Caches of meat, fish, fat, and berries were brought out. The Moose People enjoyed life.

While the people were all together they participated in community religious functions. The priest or shaman announced a service and on the appointed evening all the people crowded into the house. The shaman entered, stuck his medicine staff upright in the bough floor, and began to sing. The song was very old and told of a time when an evil shaman had died and his spirit remained to trouble the people for many months. Hunting was bad; many people were sick. Their shaman dreamed and in the dream his guardian spirit, a raven, gave instructions. He ordered the people to move their houses, to expose all their clothing, robes, and bedding skins to the winter air, and to boil all their utensils. Thus the evil spirit that plagued them was driven away. After the story all remained silent. The shaman moved, grasped his medicine staff, and stuck it upright beside the hearth. Then he dropped to all fours. His body shook and his teeth rattled. Suddenly the staff quivered and fell. The people gasped. It pointed toward the hunter's aged mother. She dropped her head in silence. The shaman arose and from his medicine pouch removed a pinch of dark powder. He sprinkled this on the fire, retrieved his staff, and left the house.

Finally the sun shone once more from behind the snow peaks. *Tcitciun* was over and now began the moon called *satco* or the Big Moon, when the days grew longer and the cold became stronger.

Family by family the People of the Moose departed to their winter hunting areas. The hunter and his kla loaded their possessions on the toboggans. The women took over and pulled the toboggans, while the two hunters set off at a trot through the snowy taiga. Their huge hunting snowshoes supported them on top of the fluffy snow cover. All day they ranged in great looping arcs away from the toboggan trail and back again. For several days they encountered no fresh moose sign.

Then the kla saw the deep double furrows of a moose trail. It was fresh. He immediately set off along it. He knew that when the hunter did not encounter his snowshoe trail at the usual meeting time, he would double back and would soon be following the same moose.

As the sun dipped below the distant snow peaks the hunter

caught up with his kla. Together they set about making camp for the night. Using their snowshoes for shovels they soon had a large pile of snow mounded up. Then they left the spot, and during the hours of fading light they reconnoitered the moose trail ahead. They saw where the moose had headed and where they, too, would go the next day.

By the time they returned to their mound the snow crystals had recombined and solidified into a relatively stable mass. Carefully they began to dig away the snow in one spot at the base of the mound. Taking turns digging, they excavated the interior of the mound until a hemispherical room some six feet in diameter was formed. They carefully cleaned out all the snow from the mossy floor, and their house was ready. They shook all their clothes and beat off all traces of snow adhering to them. Then they crawled into the house and stuffed up the door with a piece of caribou skin that was carried for the purpose.

During the subarctic night the deep cold settled over the taiga. Heat from the snow surface, from the trees, from the hares, and from the moose radiated to outer space. Trees popped and the moonlight sparkled on the frost crystals riding in the frigid air. But inside the house the two hunters slept comfortably, protected from the infinite heat sink of the sky by the thick snow layer above them, and warmed by the heat flowing from the earth beneath. During their sleep a small red-backed vole poked his head out of the moss beside them, scuttled over the floor, and dived into another tunnel.

The hunters awoke refreshed and removed the caribou-skin door to see how the day was. The snow-covered spruces towered above them into the gold and violet sky. The cold, dry air rushed into the house and replaced the warm, moist air within, which became a cloud of ice fog outside the shelter. A Canada jay glided down on outstretched wings and perched on the tip of a snowshoe stuck in the snow. The jay cocked his head and mewed softly. A raven wheeled overhead, the dense, cold air whistling through his flight feathers.

The hunters chewed on a few strips of dried meat and carefully checked their bows and bowstrings. Then they slipped their moccasined toes into the thongs of their snowshoes and once again began to trot along the moose trail.

By the time the sun was fully up they had crested a ridge and seen the moose far ahead in the valley. The kla left the trail and began a long, circuitous detour which would bring him to the moose from a different direction. The hunter waited until he saw the kla appear on the next ridge and then he, too, resumed the chase. In the calm, dense air the moose heard the kla and altered its route so that it was now heading in the general direction of where the hunters knew their families were camped. Both hunters now followed the trail from far to the side, herding the great beast along.

When the sun reached its highest point the hunters increased their pace, and the moose did likewise. But a moose cannot run for long while breaking trail through a thick snow cover. The moose would stop, its sides heaving, and look back to where the sounds of pursuit originated. Its breath spread around it as a cloud of ice fog; its trail was marked by a thin cloud of ice fog.

Finally the moose, now completely exhausted, turned and faced his pursuers. The hunters carefully closed in for the kill, for even in its exhausted state the moose was a formidable creature. A bow twanged. The moose hunched. Neither hunter moved. Before many minutes the moose's legs buckled and the great body collapsed in the snow.

After waiting for some minutes, and after touching the moose's eye with their bows to confirm its death, the two hunters began to skin the great carcass. They worked swiftly

since they had to cut up the meat before it froze into an immovable mass. Long before the carcass was dismembered the sun slipped below the snow peaks. The kla continued the butchering while the hunter stopped, cleaned his hands, and began to shovel snow into a mound for a house for the night. After the snow was heaped up he rejoined the butchering.

Much moose meat remained intact by the time dusk fell. Now the kla stopped work, cleaned his hands, and slipped on his snowshoes. He scoured the vicinity for dry wood, which he brought back to the site.

He removed his snowshoes and, using one as a shovel, he cleared the snow from a small area. Here he carefully made a small wooden platform. Next, from his fire bag he drew out the tools with which to make fire—a slab of dry birch fungus, a stick, a cord, and a mouthpiece of mussel shell into which the stick fit. The kla then sat upon one snowshoe and held the fungus between his knees. With the mouthpiece and stick in place he wrapped the cord around the stick and twirled it back and forth. The stick spun in the fungus and soon a wisp of smoke appeared. By careful blowing and swinging he soon had a flickering flame, and then a full fire, on the platform.

Before long the moose head hung, slowly twisting, by the fire. In the flickering light the two Dinje completed the dismemberment of the carcass. They buried the meat and skin in the snow and piled additional snow on top. The insulation of the snow would keep the meat from freezing too hard before the women could complete its preparation.

Their work done, the hunters made a meal of the choice meat on the moose head, relishing the tender meat of the nose. The tongue was split and roasted. After eating their fill the hunters excavated the mound of snow and completed the house. They crawled inside and slept soundly.

Next morning the hunter sped away toward the family

camp, while the kla remained to guard the meat and to prepare a site for the new family camp. As he worked, scooping the snow away from the site, Canada jays arrived to clean up the bits of meat and frozen blood. A jay tugged and pulled until a scrap broke free from the snow, then laboriously flew away with it to the thickest part of a spruce clump. Here he jammed it into a crotch and glided back for more.

The kla slipped on his snowshoes and began to bring spruce boughs and twigs to the site. Soon he had a thick floor, some fifteen feet in diameter, of spruce twigs. Next, firewood was needed. When the kla heard the distant shout of a raven, announcing the approach of the women and the toboggans, he gathered his weapons and trotted off through the forest. Hunting for meat was the never-ending task of a man.

Day by day the earth tipped more toward the sun. The snow fell from the trees and the snow under the Dinje's snowshoes became denser. Hunting became easier and the Moose People no longer existed on the thin edge of survival. The men could now spend time hunting animals other than the moose, animals that gave less return in meat for effort expended.

So the hunter's joy was great when he found, beside a thick tangle of wind-thrown spruces, a hole in the snow from which a wisp of vapor curled. Carefully he stepped toward the hole and bent to sniff the vapor. Here was the overwintering den of a black bear.

The hunter sped away, first to tell the kla, and then on a two-day trip to the region where he knew the nearest Dinje lived at this season.

Four Dinje hunters later assembled near the bear den. They were equipped with stout poles in addition to their regular weapons. Two of the strongest men stationed themselves on either side of the hole in the snow. They held two poles which they laid in the snow, one on each side of the hole. One hunter stood with spear poised, while the other probed the snow between the poles with a long sharp stick. The snow around the hole collapsed, revealing a cavity under the log tangle.

A snort finally issued from the hole, then a growl. There was more vigorous probing. Branches crackled in the hole, more grunts and growls emerged. Then the bear appeared. The two men with the poles snapped them together, imprisoning the bear's neck, and held on with all their strength. The bear lunged out of the hole, dragging the two Dinje about. Two spears flashed into his ribs. The bear rolled and, in so doing, flipped one of the pole-men into the air, causing him to lose his grip on the poles. The bear charged him. An arrow flashed. The bear crunched the man's upper arm, shook him, and then collapsed on top of him.

The other Dinje rushed in and tugged the bear's carcass away. The injured hunter lay quiet. One man cut away the sleeve to reveal an arm deeply punctured and obviously broken but in which no artery was severed. Two hunters wrapped the sleeve back around the punctures and then wrapped the arm and hand in a caribou bedding skin.

One Dinje slipped on his snowshoes and disappeared on a run toward the home camp, almost a normal day's travel away. The remaining men began to pile up snow for a house. After they had an extra-large mound built, one prepared a platform while the other began to collect firewood. When the fire was burning and their injured companion comfortable beside it, they turned their attention to the bear carcass.

They brought the hide with its thick, glossy black fur to the injured hunter and, grinning, spread it beside him. Then they ripped open the carcass, extracted the heart, and presented it to him. One Dinje sliced off thin strips of the steaming heart and gave them to the injured man to eat. By eating the bear's heart he was thus imbued with the beast's strength and courage. They themselves would not partake of the heart until the runner returned.

The carcass was soon butchered and stored beneath the snow. Slabs of meat roasted over the fire. One man unwrapped the injured arm and, taking a piece of the cooking meat, squeezed it so that the blood and juices ran into the wounds. Then he replaced the dressings.

As the day passed, the men hollowed the mound of snow and moved the injured hunter inside it. One Dinje stayed with the injured man while the other slipped on his snowshoes and disappeared among the trees. The hunt was never-ending.

Next day, before the sun had reached its highest point, the runner returned, sliding a toboggan behind him. The injured Dinje, wrapped in caribou skins, was placed in it, the bear hide over him and the bear's skull tied to the top of the toboggan curl.

Not until the following day did they reach the home camp. Here the families of the hunter and the kla had been joined by the families of the other men. The priest had been summoned by a runner and would arrive momentarily.

When he arrived all the people gathered in one house. The shaman, wrapped in the bear skin, entered and thrust his medicine staff into the bough floor. He sang an old song recounting deeds of other bear-hunters, how they had been injured and how they had been healed. He ended by adding the story of this hunt and how this hunter would likewise be healed by the power of his medicine. Then he firmly pulled on the injured arm, set the broken bone, and splinted it with wrappings of stiff, untanned moose hide. The injured man made no sound but his eyes grew dark with pain.

The shaman ordered that every third day the arm be exposed and that warmed spruce pitch be smeared over the lacerations. Then he took a pinch of fine powder from his medicine bag, sprinkled it on the fire, and left the house.

The Moose People did not move their houses back to their winter hunting range. Had not the shaman foretold, at *Tcit-ciun*, that the hunter's aged mother would die? So the men hunted moose in this locality instead. The injured hunter and his family lived well because the choice parts of all food animals went to them, as was their due.

The old mother was busy. With the aid of her daughter-in-law she made herself a new dress shirt of soft golden-brown moose skin. Her burial garments completed, the old mother took to her caribou-skin bed and never rose again. She became progressively weaker and within a week was dead.

It was now *tcit-thia-sa*, or the Moon of the Cold Winds. The sun rose due in the east and set in the west, as the days steadily lengthened. The light reflected from the snow in a million glittering tiny suns. The Polar High still maintained a tight grip on the land of the Dinje; temperatures hovered around twenty to forty below zero. The winds were not very strong but the contrast with the almost windless deep cold of winter made the chill more cutting.

The people blackened their cheeks and eyelids with charcoal in an effort to dull the blinding light. Snow conditions were perfect for hunting but the men frequently were immobilized with snow-blindness in spite of the charcoal on their cheeks. The income of fresh-killed meat declined and the people dipped into their caches of dried moose, dried fish, and fat.

The sun began its northward arc; rising out of the northeast, swinging through the southern sky, and then sliding beneath the northwestern horizon. Each day the snow compacted a bit more, each day the surface became firmer. Then twigs and leaves appeared in the *zhe-quin-zee*, and before many days the *zhe-quin-zee* were free of snow. The long days were a blinding kaleidoscope of white, pale blue, gold, and green. The food caches dwindled; some of the people began to feel hunger.

To add to their discomfort, the snow became soft and soggy during the day. When a man was able to face the blinding light and to hunt he came home exhausted and with his snowshoe netting soaked, sagging and torn, his moose-skin moccasins and leggings wet and frequently refrozen stiff and crackling. The snow was noisy to walk upon and it was a rare occasion when a hunter succeeded in stalking a moose.

Water soaked the snow above the ice on the lakes and ponds. On the rivers the current gnawed away the ice cover from below, making travel hazardous.

The ice disappeared from one small pond after another. It disappeared from the rapids. Marshes opened. Now the people could satisfy their longing for fresh meat; open marshes meant muskrats. The men eased silently through the willow thickets around the marshes. They glided their canoes across the marshes. Soon muskrat carcasses hung, spinning, above the fires. But muskrats are small pickings compared to moose, and the people's hunger was only dulled, not satisfied.

The rivers broke up; ice blocks thundered and shrieked as they churned downstream. The people moved to their fish camps, set up their weirs—and waited. They dared not leave the fish camps for extended moose or sheep hunts because the silvery flood might come at any moment, and when it came every able-bodied Dinje was needed to harvest the crop.

For days they waited. There was an occasional grayling and even some ling, but the thrashing mass of migrating whitefish and salmon did not come. The people searched their old caches for scraps of meat; they were even reduced to the indignity of hunting red squirrels for food.

The hunter brought to camp three small red squirrels. Even though he and his family were ravenous the laws of partnership decreed that these food animals were to be shared with the kla and his family. As the two families roasted the pitifully small bits of meat they heard a raven shout from upstream. Did this mean a moose? No, the raven's shout was that which indicated man. All the people were here in camp; these must be strangers.

The people ran to the river's edge to greet the strangers. Around the bend came a raft carrying five people. What strange people! Their clothing was not moose skin, they wore great black angular moccasins (Were their feet *really* that big?), and their faces were hidden behind bushy growths of hair. And what a load the raft carried! They must be exceedingly wealthy since these five men traveled with more belongings than were owned by all the people in the camp.

The Dinje could not understand the strangers' speech. "Lieutenant, they look friendly." "Yes, but what a sorry lot they are, not much chance of getting supplies from them. Corporal, head the raft ashore." "Yessir." The raft scraped along the bank; one of the strangers threw a rope to a Dinje man, who snubbed it around a tree. The people formed a semicircle around the strangers. The shaman advanced, stuck his medicine staff into the ground, and began the song of welcome. "What's he saying, Lieutenant?" "I'm sure I don't know. Give him some beads anyway, Corporal." One of the strangers handed the shaman a tiny box. The shaman bowed and reached behind him. One of the people thrust into his hand a precious long-dried piece of whitefish. The shaman handed this to the stranger who accepted it gingerly. "What's this stuff, Lieutenant Allen? Do you want it, sir?" "No, but put it into the box and we'll throw it out later. Hand out beads to all the adult males; we must keep them pacified. Perhaps we can later trade for supplies."

So the hunter, his kla, and the other men received packages of beads and marveled at this display of wealth. By signs the kla invited the strangers to his fire, where he seated them in the places of honor and presented them the three roasted squirrels. "Rats!" exclaimed the Corporal. "What kind of people are these that try to feed us rats?" "Obviously a sign of disdain, Corporal; they are not so friendly as they seemed to be. Give that chief a small sack of flour as a peace offering and we'll be on our way before we get scalped." "Yes, sir."

The people, puzzled by the strangers' sudden departure, followed them to the riverbank. When it was evident that they really intended to leave, some of the men waded into the river and pulled up several poles of the weir so that the raft could float through.

It disappeared downstream, leaving a puzzled group of Dinje watching it. The shaman held the bag of flour and examined it closely. He opened the bag and drew out a pinch of the white powder. He tasted it and spat. He took another pinch and tossed it on a nearby fire. It burned satisfactorily, so he closed the sack and took it into the house.

A shout from one of the men replacing the poles brought everyone back to the river. Fish! The first dimples appeared on the river's surface. By the next day the run was full and the trap was lifted, emptied, and reset over and over. The heap of fish before the women grew higher. The air was redolent of the smell of fish. Fires burned to heat the rocks that boiled the water in the great bark kettles. The curly-tailed dogs glutted themselves on fish entrails and scraps; then they collapsed in the sun to sleep. The people likewise ate fresh fish and slept in the sun. Life was good.

People of the Moose

When the run slackened and the drying racks bent under their load of fish the shaman announced a service. That night the people, laughing and joking, crowded into one house. The shaman entered, stuck his medicine staff into the floor, and began to sing. He sang of the people's hardships during the time of brilliant light, of the breakup, of muskrat hunting, of the strangers' visit, and finally of the exceptionally heavy run of fish. Then he dropped onto all fours, quivered and rolled onto his side, his eyes staring and his jaws clenched. The people made no sound. After long minutes a baby whimpered and its mother clapped her hand over its mouth. The fire burned lower and was only a bed of coals when the shaman began to twitch. His eyes rolled, then focused, and he staggered upright, his face pale.

"People of the Moose, listen. I have journeyed far. I saw the great Tsa-o-sha when he lived among us as a man. I journeyed back to the present and then into the future. I saw many strangers such as those we saw recently. They swarmed over our country, their great hard moccasins stamped out the moose tracks. They rooted in the mud and gravel of the streams. The air was filled with smoke; the taiga burned. The moose were all killed, the caribou disappeared. Even the fish never came, for the strangers at one place had filled the river with rocks and earth and had created a lake in which the fish became lost. And listen, Dinje, you were no more. The People of the Moose were scattered, and those few remaining were sick and starving and were slaves to the strangers."

The shaman removed a pinch of the strangers' white powder from his medicine bag and sprinkled this on the fire. He retrieved his staff and left the house. The people remained, staring into the dying embers of their fire.

Life Goes On

On the north shore of the Fond du Lac River, in northern Saskatchewan, there was a high rock bluff. Three hundred yards inland the land sloped down to a fine, mature spruce forest. The snow under the spruces lay fluffy and soft. This was not the wet, sticky snow of the temperate zone but the soft, downy snow of the taiga. Its surface was not regular and even; around the base of every tree it dipped to form a deep, bowl-shaped depression, for the tree limbs up above caught and held some of the falling snow. The needly twigs of the spruces were so loaded with snow that the tips bent far downward. We cannot talk about the snow features with any facility, because our language evolved in a misty maritime climate, far from this clean, dry snow. We lack the proper words. The local Chipewyan Indian tongue, which evolved here in the taiga, has words for these things. The Chipewyan call the bowl-shaped depressions *day-chen-yath-do-dee*, and the snow that remains on the trees they call *day-chen-kay-silch-tran*.

This fluffy forest snow is one of the best natural insulators. Above the snow the temperature was thirty below zero, and frost formed on the ruff of your parka hood. A few inches beneath the snow the temperature was a comparatively warm twenty-three degrees. The base of the snow cover had assumed a peculiar granular form, a fragile lattice of ice crystals. In our own misty tongue we call this structure "depth hoar," being forced to compare it with the hoarfrost of a maritime winter. The Chipewyans know it by a more precise and expressive word, *yath-k-ona*, pronouncing the *k* as a hard, sharp, separate syllable. Right at the very base of the snow cover, the *yath-k-ona* separated into pillars and columns with extensive empty spaces in between.

Here it was almost dark, for twenty-eight inches of snow transmits less than one per cent of the light that falls on it. The air was calm and saturated with water vapor. The temperature had not varied here more than five degrees in the past month. The delicate pillars and columns of the *yath-k-ona* rested on the mossy floor of the forest. The moss, though frozen, was loose and friable, and its featherlike branches could be pushed aside easily even by the sharp-nosed, twittering shrews.

In this world under the snow, sharp eyesight counts for nothing, long springy legs are useless, the flexible funnel-like ears of caribou would be worthless. What matters is the number of impregnable refuges you have, and knowing the exact distance you are from each one. A keen sense of hearing is not as important as a keen sense of *vibrations*, for the warnings of danger here are in the thud of approaching footfalls transmitted by the snow.

In this patch of spruce forest a small mouselike rodent, known as the red-backed vole or *Clethrionomys gapperi*, lived in a series of interconnecting tunnels that ran through the moss. This particular vole had short legs and tail, was about five and a half inches long, and weighed just about as much as two half-dollars. His fur was thick and soft, yellowish-brown on the sides and a rich dark red on the back. His eyesight was limited to a few yards, but keen eyes are not needed in this world beneath the snow. His hearing was good, but not nearly as good as that, say, of a red squirrel. His contact with the world about him was primarily through his sense of smell, which was very keen, and his sense of touch and vibration. His windows on the world were vibrissae, the long sensitive whiskers that projected around his face, and the special short, sensitive hairs which stuck out from his wrists. They were perfectly adapted to the environment in which he lived; he needed little more.

By our standards, the world of this vole was not very large. It encompassed a little more than a quarter of an acre. Within this quarter acre there were eight large spruce trees, numerous willows, five paper birches, five dead and rotting logs nearly covered by moss, and one prostrate spruce that had been blown down several years back. The vole avoided the vicinity of the large spruces, because the ground beneath the day-chen-yath-do-dee, lacking a thick, protective snow cover, was bitterly cold to his sensitive feet. The willows were better; they had small tunnels under the roots which could be used in times of emergency. The rotting logs were also channeled with tunnels. But the finest refuges of all were the gnarled and twisted roots of the paper birches, among which the vole and his predecessors had made many tortuous tunnels. During the summer the wind-thrown spruce lay too far above the moss to be of much value, but now about it there were whole galleries of empty spaces under the snow. During the summer the vole was limited to the moss tunnels, but the snow cover provided his world with a third dimension; now he could tunnel upward to the snow surface as well as move anywhere on the moss surface. The latticelike structure of the *yath-k-ona* allowed him to slip about with ease.

The vole had learned every fallen leaf on the moss surface, every projecting stem and trunk, each refuge hole, since he had found this home range vacant last August, shortly after he had been weaned. Many years ago a windstorm had strained one of the paper birches and broken a root. The broken end eventually rotted away and left a cavity in the soil. This cavity had been taken over as a nesting site by an ancestral vole, and the nest was now thick-walled and warm.

The vole had well-used trails radiating from this nest to all parts of his home range. One trail led to a food cache inside a rotten log. As the vole scuttled back and forth over these trails, he left his scent behind him on the soil, moss, spruce needles, and twigs. Whenever he ventured beyond his usual route, he encountered the scent of another individual and retreated to more familiar surroundings. On two sides of his home range he had not encountered any stranger-scent, for the home ranges there were vacant. This was a "low mouse year," and there were many vacant home ranges throughout the forest. Still, he did not enter these vacant ranges; his needs were met within his own quarter acre, and a strong feeling pulled him back to familiar territory whenever he ventured into a tunnel that did not carry his own scent.

Because it was winter, the vole felt no urge to wander, no craving for the scent of others of his own species. It is almost always dark in the tortuous galleries and chambers of tinkling *yath-k-ona*, so he knew night and day only vaguely. There was no diurnal rhythm to his activity. He awakened from sleep curled up in the nest, felt hungry, and scuttled out to one of his food caches. Half a dozen dried blueberries satisfied him, and soon he scooted along a tunnel through the moss until he was under the wind-thrown spruces. Here the tunnel tipped sharply upward, and he emerged suddenly into a chamber that to us would be breathtakingly beautiful. The ceiling was domed, and it glowed softly with a bluish light, reflected and refracted from a million tiny prisms of ice. The walls were made of columns of yath-k-ona that sparkled and glowed. The vole accidentally brushed a column as he passed by, and the entire structure, part of the wall, collapsed with a tiny tinkling sound into a heap of pyramidal, glittering fragments.

The vole explored his system of chambers under the downed spruce, leaving his scent and so marking his ownership of it. In this fashion four hours passed, and he felt once more the gnawing sensation of hunger. Back to his food cache he went, this time using a different set of tunnels. Another meal, now with a dried cranberry added for good measure, and his hunger was satisfied. The sensation of fatigue became overpowering. He scarcely had time to scuttle back to the nest before he was overcome by sleep.

In this routine the vole lived all winter, his periods of activity recurring at four-hour intervals independent of the sun that swung across the southern sky in the strange white world above the snow. Winter was a serene time for him; no breeding urges to upset his rhythm, no sudden rain showers to soak the moss and wet his fur. The only dangerous time had been passed safely—the snow cover had built up before the bitter cold of subarctic winter settled over the region. If the insulating snow had not come in time, the moss would have been frozen hard and impenetrable, the nest incapable of sustaining comfortable warmth, and worst of all, he would have been unable to get enough to eat to keep his body temperature at a safe level. The vacant home ranges near him were empty because the previous two winters had little snow, and in one of them the snow cover did not build up in time to protect the forest floor from a cold snap of twenty-seven degrees below zero. Many voles and shrews died during that period of thermal stress.

The vole awakened from his sleep with a sudden start. His vibrissae quivered as they received vibrations through the nest wall. Then his ears picked up sounds, peculiar scrapings and grindings, and finally an undercurrent of gentle paddings and thumpings. The noise level rose to a peak and soon tapered off into silence. He sank back into slumber; this had been a disturbance on top of the snow and outside his home range, so it was of no consequence to him. The scrapings were actually the sound of a toboggan sliding through the snow; the paddings and thumpings were the footfalls of five dogs pulling the toboggan. Breaking trail on snowshoes ahead of the dogs had been a Chipewyan trapper, on his way to set out a new line of mink traps.

The vole's four-hour clock prodded ·his stomach, and it began to contract gently in hunger. He wakened, stretched, and proceeded carefully to clean his fur. It was not the human urge of vanity that made him do this, but a deeply ingrained instinct that had developed from strict necessity. Fur that is matted, greasy, or dirty loses its insulating value, and that would be disastrous for a small mammal. After working over all his fur until it stood out soft and fluffy from his body, the vole left the nest and scuttled to his nearest food cache. A dried rose hip comprised this meal. A new sound came to his ears—a delicate crunching of the snow and then a tinkling noise as *yath-k-ona* collapsed. Suddenly an overpowering musky odor filled his nostrils, and at almost the same instant a blinding pain shot through his head. His life ended.

The slim, muscular weasel with yellow-tinged white coat licked the three drops of blood that oozed from the needle punctures in the base of the vole's skull. He darted outside the food cache and rubbed his lips and cheeks against a yath-k-ona column, which immediately collapsed in a shower of ice crystals. The weasel shook the ice dust off his fur and, nose to the moss, followed the vole's trail back until he came to the nest. He darted inside, curled round and round a few times and slipped back outside. He returned to the food cache, where he pushed his nose deep into the fur of the vole's lifeless warm body. The scent was overpoweringly delicious to the weasel, for it represented all that was good in his life. Here was the food that millions of years of evolution, uncounted generations of weasels before him, had perfected his supple, muscular body to seek out and capture.

It was no accidental blundering that had led him to the vole. The weasel, too, had a home range, one of several miles' circumference. It took him three weeks, occasionally as long as a month, to make a complete circuit. On this particular trip he had shifted his usual route only a few yards to investigate the mound of snow that covered the wind-thrown spruce. Plunging under the surface of the snow, he entered the glittering galleries of yath-k-ona under the windfall's dead, dry branches. Here his nose picked up the faint scent left by the vole's presence several hours earlier. All the hunting skills perfected by evolution came into play as he followed the scent through the tunnels that turned and twisted among the fragile crystal lattice. Occasionally, in his eagerness, he brushed against one of the pillars, and it collapsed with a tiny tinkling. This was the only warning the vole had heard.

The weasel gripped the vole carcass with his teeth and, turning, slipped out of the food cache. He made his way to the nest, heedless now of the crashing and tinkling he caused by pushing the vole's body through the tunnels. He dropped the carcass outside the nest, slipped inside, turned around and popped his head out again. He pulled the carcass to the nest

opening and began to feed. First he crunched through the paper-thin bone of the skull and removed the brains, making small smacking sounds as he licked the warm juices. Next he ripped open the abdomen and gripped the liver with his needle-sharp teeth. He tugged and the liver, spleen, heart, and lungs slid from the opening. These he gulped almost frantically, for their taste continually spurred him on. He did not realize it, but a craving for minerals and vitamins caused him to eat first those parts of the vole's body which contained the largest amount of them.

After consuming the pluck, the weasel rested for a few minutes. Then he began to eat again, more methodically this time, without the frantic haste of his first feeding. As he fed, crunching the small bones and stripping the larger ones, he peeled off the vole skin by pushing it ahead with his nose. Finally there remained only the feet, tail and skin, which was turned inside out like a hastily removed glove. The weasel licked his fur carefully, removing all traces of blood or body juices. Then he darted outside the nest and rolled and cavorted in the loose yath-k-ona. After he was clean and all traces of the vole were gone from his fur, he stretched and slipped back inside the appropriated nest. Here he curled up and slept the sleep of one who had completed a full day's work and been rewarded with a satisfying meal.

When the weasel awakened hours later, he sniffed carefully all about the nest but could discover no additional scents that aroused the hunting instinct in him. He darted from the nest, followed his trail back to the wind-thrown spruce and then up through the snow cover to the outside world. As he poked his head through the soft, fluffy, fresh-fallen layer, he blinked at the bright light. After his eyes stopped watering, he popped out onto the snow surface. His body sank several inches into the snow. He gathered his feet under him and leaped, landing with all four feet together. This method of locomotion, like his hunting skills, had been perfected through evolutionary time. It was well adapted for traveling over and through the soft, yielding snow, but it was quite tiring. So when the weasel came to the hard smooth trail which the dog team and toboggan had packed down, he followed it almost automatically.

After the meal of fresh vole and the long sleep, the weasel was full of vim and well-being. He bounced along the toboggan trail, a slim lithe shape that was gone almost as soon as it appeared.

Suddenly a strange odor filled the air. The weasel stopped, stood on his hind legs and turned his head this way and that, trying to locate the source of the scent. This was a new smell —it was not vole; it was not hare; it was not Canada jay. Neither was it red squirrel. Suddenly a slight movement caught his eye. Instantly all his hunting responses clicked into action, and the weasel made a flying leap toward the moving object. As he came down onto the snow surface, feet together, he felt something hard under them. Before he could jump again, the snow on each side of him exploded and the steel jaws of a mink trap crushed his shoulders and hips. He screamed in pain, threw his head around and splintered his teeth against the steel jaws.

The instant after the jaws snapped shut, the trap flew up in the air as the bent branch to which it was attached was released and straightened out. The trap swung slowly back and forth, pendulum fashion, and then came to rest. A few drops of blood dripped, steaming, from the weasel's nostrils. The last drop formed, thickened, and froze without falling. The cold steel jaws of the trap soon sucked the heat from the weasel's body and radiated it to the sky. Before an hour passed, the weasel's body was frozen solid.

Eleven days elapsed. The Chipewyan trapper returned along his trapline. Last evening a Canada jay had glided down from a nearby branch and clung for an instant to the weasel's body. A peck on each side of the head removed the frozen eyeballs, but the jay lost his grip and fluttered off. Before he could return, the distant hoot of a horned owl caused him to fly to a dense spruce clump nearby, and when he had regained his composure, it was too dark to see the weasel's carcass any more.

The Indian muttered under his breath when he saw the weasel's crushed and frozen carcass. The skin was nearly worthless, and the trap had been out of operation for a long time. He wondered how many valuable mink had wandered safely by because the trap was already full. Still, the weasel skin was worth a few cents, so he removed the carcass carefully from the trap and tossed it into the toboggan. He reset the trap, then sprinkled a few drops of fish oil on the swinging tuft of feathers that had attracted the weasel's attention, and the set was ready again.

That night, sitting on his thick bed of spruce twigs, the Indian carefully thawed the carcass and peeled off the skin. Before it froze again, he slipped the skin over a stretcher made from two peeled willow twigs and packed it in the toboggan. The carcass was tossed into the snow, where it was eventually found by a shrew who would feast on it for an entire month before it was consumed.

The Chipewyan had not had very good luck with his traps. Only four mink had been taken, and one of these was an old male whose pelt was scarred and worth only half as much as the others. Therefore the Indian carefully dried the weasel skin along with the mink.

Upon his return to the village, he took them all to The Bay store. The manager blew on the mink skins to examine the underfur, did some figuring on a slip of paper, and named a price to the Indian. The Indian shrugged his shoulders. After all, to whom else could he sell them? The manager grinned,

148

added fifty cents to the total to pay for the weasel skin and gave the signed slip of paper to the Chipewyan. Out in the store the Indian bought flour and baking powder for his daily bannock, tea for his noon boil-ups, a can of tobacco and a pack of cigaret papers, while his wife picked out some clothing for the youngsters. "How much left?" he asked the clerk. The clerk slowly totaled the bill. "Fifty cents to go," he answered. The Indian picked up a box of twenty-two-caliber shells. "This will do it," he said, and gathering his supplies, he left the store.

The twenty-two rifle is the universal gun in the taiga. It is light and inexpensive and uses cheap ammunition. It is not powerful enough, and some game escapes wounded; but the white man treats the game supply as inexhaustible, so why should the Indian act differently?

On his next trip around the trapline, the Chipewyan shot seven spruce grouse with his twenty-two. On the following trip the rifle gained him five grouse and two snowshoe hares. On the trip after that he shot all the remaining shells at a band of five caribou. None fell, but two does were wounded in the paunch. In the days before his contact with the white man, a Chipewyan would have trailed the wounded caribou for days, until his pursuit was successful. The white man's schools, churches, and stores had eroded his culture so much that the ancestral law was forgotten. The Indian did not follow the caribou.

The two wounded caribou soon stiffened and became lame. One lay down under a tree, and the other stumbled and fell over the trunk of a wind-thrown spruce nearby. Neither ever regained her feet, for the normal action of fermentation within the paunches soon caused the contents to flood the peritoneal cavity. Death was slow and painful. Since both these caribou were pregnant, actually four animals died.

149

When the one caribou fell over the wind-thrown spruce, her body crushed the snow and *yath-k-ona* beneath her. A fresh snowfall covered the carcass and hid it from the jays and ravens.

Many days later a shrew thrust his sensitive snout through the jumble of ice crystals. He nibbled on the frozen caribou tongue, tentatively, until he got the meat taste, then ferociously and hungrily. Before long a vole, tunneling through the ice maze, reached the carcass. He tasted a bit of the tongue, too, and gnawed off a larger piece. After satisfying his hunger for protein, he caught the faint scent of another vole. Because spring was approaching, he felt a dim stirring of the urge to meet another of his kind. Whether he needed to fight or love, he did not know. His exact response would be governed by the actions and scent of the vole he encountered. The scent remained faint, but finally he found the source, a bit of frozen and dried skin with a few scraps of bone attached lying beside the entrance of a well-made vole nest. The vole slipped into the nest and made himself at home.

This drama of life and death, of food-searching, killing and eating has no end. It continues with the unceasing cycle of the seasons. All living creatures enter it for a few scenes—the vole, the weasel, the jay, the caribou, the Indian, and the white man—while the eternal snow whispers down through the spruces, winter after winter.

Homestead

Springtime flooded over the taiga. The snow cover grew granular, shrank and pulled away from the qamaniq; it finally retreated to shady spots on the north sides of thick spruce clumps. The moss changed from yellowish to a vivid green as life quickened within the plants. Mosquitoes hummed and whined in the warm air.

Another sound pulsated through the forest—a roar that swelled louder and nearer. Through the roar could now be heard a cacophony of crackling and popping and the screech of tortured metal. The roar slackened and then began again.

The huge D-8 cat lowered its blade, bellowed its exhaust, and clattered forward. Spruces shuddered, their roots tore loose from the wet soil, and the trees tumbled and snapped as the steel monster pushed them away.

The living carpet of moss was peeled up in curling sheets. The lichens, soft, succulent, and lush, were pulped under the steel-cleated tracks of the cat. A hare, heavy with young, fled from her home range and away from the destruction. A red-backed vole, tied by instinct to its home range, was sheared asunder.

Up and back, up and back, roared the machine. Slowly the horizon grew flat as the spruce spires toppled. The tortured carcasses of the spruces, the birches, the tamaracks, the aspens, the great rolls of moss and peat, and the small bloody stains that were once living voles and shrews, were pushed and jammed by the great steel blade into long windrows or berms. Here and there along the berm the cat operator left, as the supreme insult, an untouched spruce, somehow spared temporarily, with the shattered carcasses of its fellows heaped about it.

And this willful destruction of the wealth of centuries of ecological succession was done, not by sinister political plotters, but by well-meaning and honest men with the help of official government subsidies to buy the D-8 cat and hire the operator. Between the berms now clanked subsidy-bought farm machinery that ripped and tore the fragile podzol, drilled myriad furrows and injected the countless alien seeds of oats and barley, and repacked the fluffy podzol particles.

The churning by the farm implements allowed the long-hoarded store of scarce nutrients to be released. The oats and the barley, and later the grass, sucked in these suddenly re-leased nutrients and grew lush and green. The new homestead farm was, to untrained eyes, a beautiful sight with fields of ripening grain rippling under the subarctic sun, with placid Holstein cows grazing on the vivid green pastures.

When the long subarctic winter came, the homesteader kept the cows in the barn. No longer was there lush grass for their feed; they ate bale after bale of hay. They also ate bag after bag of concentrate which was shipped into the subarctic from the temperate zone far away. Before the winter had passed the homesteader was forced to negotiate a loan at the bank in order to purchase more concentrate and even hay from the "outside."

But in the taiga, the native moose fed unconcernedly on the frost-brittle willow, birch, and aspen twigs. No barn, no concentrate, no hay was necessary for the moose. And if one calculates the acreage of subarctic grass and hay, plus the acreage of temperate zone farmland required to produce the concentrate and imported hay, one arrives at the startling conclusion that moose produce meat in the subarctic cheaper than do cows. The relation also holds for milk production, since only about five per cent of a cow's energy intake can be retrieved as milk energy.

With the protecting forest gone the landscape was tundra-like. Winds could now reach down and toss the snow about. Not far away, within the protection of the remaining taiga, roads remained usable all winter, but the winds howled across the bare homestead fields. The unprotected farm road became choked again and again with drifts as high as a car. More of the homesteader's scarce cash went to buy fuel oil to heat his wind-chilled house. Within the house his wife grew irritable at being confined. The clear plastic heat shields over the windows popped and crackled in the wind and added to her irritation.

Winters passed. The sun each spring melted the snow quicker from the open fields than from the forested areas. The meltwater trickled downhill, finding each year the same tracks and ruts. The fluffy podzol lasted only one breakup and then it was gone. The soft subsoil eroded with the relentless trickle of melting snow. Gullies formed around the house, along the road, down to the barn, and on across the fields. From the air one could see the incipient trace of that trademark of subsistence agriculture—a dendritic pattern of erosional gullies.

As the dry taiga summer passed, the homesteader decided to burn berm. Before the day was out, the air for miles downwind was hazy and redolent of the smoke of burning spruce and moss. This homesteader was relatively careful of fire; others were not so careful. North of the homestead a berm fire swept out of control and roared over several square miles of forest. Some men chuckled that the fire was deliberately put out of control, and who could say no? Why be so careful, they said, it was just worthless bushland that burned; besides, burning made it all the easier to clear.

After a few years the small store of long-hoarded nutrients in the podzol was depleted, and the homesteader was forced to spend even more money on imported fertilizers. In addition, the fields were becoming difficult to work with mechanical equipment. Hummocks developed, a regular polygonal pattern of shallow ditches surrounding raised areas. Once more the government-sponsored D-8 cat clattered and roared over the land; its great blade smoothed out the fields.

For several years the homesteader worked the land, fighting the snow-clogged road in winter and the ever-shrinking crop yields in the summer. Then one day, while he was mowing hay, the earth opened up beneath the tractor's wheels. Down crashed the tractor into a thermokarst pit where the frozen subsoil had finally melted away because the insulating moss cover was no longer present. Luckily the homesteader was unhurt. He clambered out of the pit and stalked to the house. This was the last straw.

Before many days the "farm" was abandoned; the homesteader had admitted defeat and moved to town. His wife sang for joy at the thought of a regular income.

But what was defeated? Was it only the homesteader? The land now had no protective forest cover; it lay eroded and hummocky, covered with a jungle of tall purple-flowered fireweed. The fireweed grew taller where the berms once lay in long strips and where their nutrients were concentrated. Eventually willows and aspens sprouted on the abandoned and gullied fields; then the moose and hares returned.

The homesteader's house, unused, grew damp; the roof rotted and fell in. The farm equipment rusted beside the barn. The tractor still lay at the bottom of the thermokarst pit. The once productive taiga was now an ecological slum. From a dense willow thicket came the white-crowned sparrow's sad, sweet song.

The Boom

In the dim prehistory of North America, after the continental glacier had melted, the scoured bedrock ridges and troughs of the Canadian Shield remained bare and sterile. Many thousands of daily exposures to the sun's energy broke down the bare rock and it became covered with chips, then finer chips and eventually soil; horsetails colonized the soil and were finally superseded by a thin, struggling taiga of scattered spruce trees. Between the spruces were bushes of Labrador tea and dwarf birch, and under them the basic carpet of lichens and mosses. Because of the low summer temperatures, the fallen leaves and needles did not rot when they died and fell. They compacted and turned to peat. Eventually, after more thousands of exposures to the sun's energy, the once bare rock was hidden by a thick mat of peat, on top of which grew the taiga.

The topmost layer of peat was riddled by the tunnels and

runways of red-backed voles and shrews. The Labrador tea, the dwarf birch, and the willows and alders were clipped and barked by snowshoe hares. Every few years a moose would spend the winter here, pulling down the birches and alders to strip the tender new growth. And twice each year, in autumn and in spring, the caribou came, with hoofs clacking and popping, on their migration to and from their wintering range. Each caribou walked with its muzzle close to the ground. It pulled a clump of lichens here, stripped the leaves from a stem of dwarf birch there, and pulled another clump of lichen farther on. Above the caribou a red squirrel shelled a spruce cone and the extra seeds fluttered down to the ground. Some seeds happened to fall onto the spots where the lichen cover had been broken by the caribou's feeding. These seeds were the ones that would germinate and grow to succeed the present adult trees. Not many seeds were successful, but because of the low energy budget of the taiga not many new seedlings were necessary to reproduce the forest.

One summer day a helicopter fluttered overhead. From its belly hung a cable which supported a shining cylinder. The helicopter thundered on, then turned and made other passes back and forth over the area. Later in the summer it returned. This time it landed on a small open ridge. Two men climbed out and unloaded a stack of boxes and bundles. The helicopter roared aloft and fluttered out of sight.

The men pitched a tent and set up camp. Then they unpacked the boxes and assembled a portable power drill. The roar of its engine echoed over the forest. The drill bit and chattered into the rocky ridge. Its vibrations caused bubbles of marsh gas to rise to the surface of a pond in the valley beside the ridge. After a week the helicopter returned and the men loaded into it many long rock cores, each protected in its own box.

Far to the south, in Toronto, a stock ticker clattered and spewed out a strip of tape. A perspiring young man wrote figures on a huge blackboard that covered one end of the room. In the brokers' seats one man leaned back and whispered to another, "Watch No-Ferrous; it's up three points since yesterday." His partner nodded and, later, quietly left his seat.

Next day No-Ferrous climbed five more points. Orders to buy this stock came from investors, speculators, and suckers. Some of their money lined the pockets of the brokers, some circled around among the other habitual stock-players, but some ended up in the bank account of No-Ferrous, Ltd. Thus the company was able to send another helicopter crew to the ridge in the taiga. Other companies and individuals joined the "good thing."

Helicopters roared in, dumped their loads and took off again. A small lake nearby was roiled with the floats of Beavers, Otters, and a variety of other types of aircraft.

The peaty valleys were churned to a pulp. Spruces that had taken a hundred years to grow were cut to provide corner posts for claims, for firewood, and for corduroy roads. The mining camp was booming. Rock drills roared and chattered, bulldozers scraped the thousand-year-old peat into windrows and churned the lichens into powder.

Then the inevitable happened—fire. Someone touched off the trash dump and sparks ignited a bulldozed dry spruce top nearby. Flames hissed through the dry lichens, roared up through the resinous branches of another spruce. The smoke rose thick, white, and acrid.

"Hey, lookit the fire!" "Yeah, good thing the wind is away from camp." "That fire sure saves us the trouble of dozing off the overburden there."

The rock drills and bulldozers continued their work. "Cat

158

time" was too expensive to be wasted making a firelane, although an hour's work would have contained the fire. The fire spread through the summer-dry lichen and moss, roaring whenever it turned a spruce tree to a torch. By the end of the day the flames had blackened a hundred acres; by the next day, a square mile. Unfought, the fire burned for a week, when chance rain showers dampened it out. Twenty thousand acres lay charred.

More cores were flown out. The outline of the ore body

was delimited. The prospectors whose claims lay outside this area drifted away, their tents and tools abandoned. The camp population shrank as winter approached. The boom collapsed.

The days grew shorter; willow leaves turned sere and brown. On the rocky ridges the patches of bearberry glowed scarlet. The outriders of the herds of migrating caribou arrived from the north. They encountered the huge freshly burned area and turned aside. On each previous migration five thousand caribou had spent about ten days here in the fall and ten days again in the spring. But caribou could no longer live in the burned area. Thus the total caribou lives were reduced by about a hundred thousand caribou-days per year.

Moose no longer spent the winter there; squirrels were gone; hares were gone; voles and shrews were gone. The bare rock ridges lay exposed to the howling winds and drifting snow, as bare and sterile as when the glaciers had melted. The total productivity of Canada had been reduced.

Far to the south, in Toronto, a Deputy Minister rose to address a meeting of the Board of Trade. He spoke in glowing terms of the increased annual rate of economic growth. He dwelt at length on the qualities of hard work, vision, and aggressive drive that characterized the business leaders of the industry. Then on behalf of the Board of Trade he presented its annual award to one who had done the most during the past year to exemplify these qualities, the President of No-Ferrous, Ltd.

This is the story of the passenger pigeon,
   being retold with the caribou.
This is the story of the heath hen,
   being retold with the grizzly bear.
This is the story of the Michigan white pine,
   being retold with the Alaska white spruce.
This is the story of the eroded, bare red hills of Georgia,
   being retold with the burned and bare rocky bones
   of the earth in northern Saskatchewan.

WHY?
DON'T WE EVER LEARN?

Vision of the Future

The voles, the hares, the lynx, the moose, and the other animals lived successfully in the taiga through millennia because they had evolved as interdependent parts of a living community. The People of the Moose had also evolved as members of this community. Thus they meshed into the complex interplay of energy exchanges and were also successful. All these species were ecologically viable without conscious effort on their parts.

Northern ecosystems are easily upset by relatively slight disturbances. Because plants grow so slowly in the North, once the ecosystem has been knocked out of balance it takes a long, long time to recover. Such ecosystems are termed fragile by comparison with, for example, the deciduous forest ecosystem, which is relatively tough. It follows that the use or management of such fragile ecosystems (as contrasted with simple exploitation) would be quite a delicate business. Considerable information is needed about amounts of vegetation produced by various plant associations, population sizes of various animal species, reproductive rates of animal species, rates of natural mortality, and so on. From such a mass of figures the productivity of the ecosystem could be calculated. Once this is known then the optimum harvest of each species can be worked out.

Such integrated programs of rational use require techniques that are clearly more difficult and sophisticated than shooting a man into space. Since rational use is more difficult, governments have, by default, chosen the easier route of exploitation and extraction. These activities require only regulation of humans and are therefore infinitely easier to administer; they do not require the constant research and delicate management necessary for a sustained yield from the entire ecosystem. There is no indication that either the United States or the Canadian government is prepared to invest the manpower and funds needed for such long-term research and management.

A striking paradox is the fact that our own culture, for all its vaunted scientific achievements, has not been able to find or make a successful ecological adjustment to the Northland. We possess some of the knowledge needed to begin this adjustment but we have yet to produce an ecological Darwin to synthesize our knowledge, pinpoint our errors, and delimit an ecologically successful role for us and for our descendents.

Biological knowledge is, of course, the key to our successful adjustment to the environment. In addition, there are philosophical and psychological facets to the successful adjustment. These are the aspects wherein our own culture has been such a dismal ecological failure. For example, it is obvious that such concepts as *game*, *crop*, *resource*, *land ownership*, *predator*, *property rights*, and so on, require, in the

North, quite different emotional and legal implications than they do in temperate regions. Thus the laws and governmental frameworks in which these concepts are enmeshed should be different in the North.

It is not enough to bemoan the passing of the Pristine Northern Wilderness or to sing the praises of each successful species. This is actually only criticism. Those who have specialized knowledge of the northland must criticize constructively and point out ecologically viable routes for our culture to follow.

Let us project ourselves into the future and see how some of these ecologically viable routes would appear.

* * *

The temperate zone, long plagued by the sweltering density of its human population, had grown old and tired. Its soils were eroded and heavily contaminated with the residues of the last century's disastrous flirtation with biocides. The soil productivity had declined so that the standard of living of the human population had also dropped, although within historic times it had been something about which politicians boasted.

Thus the Northland was thrown upon its own devices, to sink or swim. Fortunately, in the latter years of the twentieth century, after the epochal rearrangement of governmental power in the United States and Canada which followed the reapportionment of legislative bodies, the temperate zone had received a belated reform of land-use practices.

These reforms were almost too late for the temperate zone, but their influence was great in the North. Traditional concepts of land ownership, inheritance, and responsibility changed so that no longer could one man own and despoil his land for personal profit, no longer could a corporation destroy a valley for the flakes of gold beneath the surface. The ecological effects of such reforms were dramatic. Rational utilization schemes which heretofore had been mere pipe dreams became realities. Sustained-yield forestry flourished under the 150-year rotation required in the taiga. With sustained yield came the incentives for research on the genetics of white spruce and birch, for research on photoperiodic ecotypes of these timber trees.

By mid-twenty-first century the climate was in the midst of another cold cycle. The sea ice of the Arctic Ocean was once again as thick as when Nansen had measured it on the voyage of the *Fram*. Colder winters brought less snow to the taiga, and solifluction processes increased in intensity. The summer growing season was shorter. Potatoes and grains could now be grown in only a few localities.

As the climate chilled, it became more difficult to keep the traditional domestic animals in the taiga. Dairy cows required heated quarters for longer periods; hay and feed became more difficult to grow and more expensive. Beef cattle became rare and finally disappeared. Hens' eggs once again were the rare objects they had been in the old days.

Offsetting these regressive changes were other changes that could only be described as progressive. The rationalized forestry already mentioned had profound ecological effects. Control of wildfire was an important innovation. With the virtual disappearance of uncontrolled fire there eventually came a time when moose declined in numbers, since moose populations are dependent on early successional stages of the taiga.

The natural decline in numbers of wild moose, together with the pioneering success of moose domestication in the Pechora-Ilych National Park in the USSR, and later in Newfoundland and Labrador, provided the incentive for the spread of moose farming. In North America the increase in moose farms was slow, because the cultural background of careful, personalized animal husbandry had been almost lost during the hundred years of the heyday of the automobile and the tractor. But now the great beasts were everywhere; their rich, tangy milk was easily obtained in all stores, and most northerners lived on domestic moose meat. The cheese made from moose milk was almost unobtainable locally, however, since most of it was shipped to the affluent countries in Africa and South America, where it commanded high prices as a delicacy.

The taiga had always been the land of berries. Cooperative research at the Baikal Biological Station and the University of Mackenzie had developed genetic varieties of several kinds of berries whose increased yield and more favorable growth-form made them suitable for cultivation and machine harvesting. Commercial canneries sprang up, and great quantities of canned berries and jam were shipped all over the North.

The "river-flat" areas in central Alaska now supported vast fields of cloudberries, which huge picking machines lumbered over at harvest time. Most of the cloudberries were destined, not for jam but for lakka, the potent brandylike drink which had originated in ancient Finland. Now it had worldwide favor, and the cloudberry growers and distillers worked full time.

Other fields grew rows of low, bushy plants with drooping, pinnately compound leaves. At harvest time machines fingered the soil, scooped out the plants, and separated the thick, fleshy roots. These plants were highly modified descendants of a species that in the old days was known commonly as "Indian potato" (Hedysarum). The enlarged roots, rich in carbohydrates, were now a staple food, used not only potato-fashion but also as flour for the famous "Indian bread." A strong competitor as a source of carbohydrates were "cedar nuts," the seeds of the stone pine, Pinus pumilis. Intensive genetic selection, plus radiation-induced mutation, had modified the wild sprawling tree into a domesticated variety. Not only could it be harvested by machines but the yield of rich, oily seeds was far greater than formerly. Great orchards of "cedar" bushes covered many thousands of acres. Because of their low-growing habit they were completely hidden in winter by the protective snow cover.

An important industry in the northwestern parts of the American taiga was now furniture manufacture. Most of these beautiful pieces were made of diamond willow. In former days diamond willow had been merely a curiosity for fashioning into lamp stands. In the early days of the twenty-first century Dr. Alfred John, the Athapaskan biologist, solved the dual problems of willow genetics plus inoculation with the pattern-causing fungus to change the willows from scrubby bushes to quick-growing trees that yielded the beautiful blond wood with the varied patterns. After being turned and finished the wood was chemically treated to make it hard and strong. For his now classic work Dr. John had received the Olaus Murie Prize, the Northland's most coveted award.

The rational schemes for utilization of the taiga did not come into being overnight. Many legislative battles were fought and lost before ecological reason prevailed. As the climate became more rigorous, however, the more rabid exploiters had departed for warmer climes. At this time occurred one of the major events in Northern history—the Tenth International Biological Program. This cooperative effort lasted for five years and concentrated on the productivity of the taiga and tundra. The recommendations of the Tenth I.B.P. were widely acclaimed. The one that undoubtedly had the most far-reaching result required all members of Northern legislative bodies to have had ecological training.

Thus the legislators could appreciate the necessity of control areas to appraise the effects of the many management and utilization schemes. In addition to the world-famous Arctic Wilderness Area (originally known as the Arctic National

Wildlife Range) there were a number of others. On these protected areas there were continuous measurements of the fluctuating levels of productivity in the entire ecosystem, the changes in nutritional content of the native vegetation and the cyclic changes in animal populations. These natural changes were used to assess the effectiveness of the changes brought about by man's schemes.

Not all the taiga was cultivated; there were vast areas where the human population was virtually absent. There were fur management areas that encompassed hundreds of square miles, forest management areas of similar size, and even vast regions left untouched. Many areas, formerly decimated, had been reclaimed. The ancient piles of bare rocks left by the primitive gold-dredging operations had been smoothed out and replanted. Most of these areas had now progressed to mature stands of timber and had been incorporated in other management areas. One important change was that such destruction of the landscape could no longer occur, since placer and dredge mining had long ago been outlawed.

A network of roadways connected the centers of human activity. But no more did dense, choking clouds of dust arise and no longer had one to dodge chuckholes in frost-heaved pavement. The development of a flexible road-surfacing material made northern vehicle travel a pleasure. The good roads allowed easy exchange of products and materials between different regions.

There was little above-ground evidence for some of the newer settlements. Instead of constantly battling the more rigorous climate, some towns avoided it and were constructed inside plastic domes on the bottoms of large, deep lakes. Here they were surrounded by water never colder than about thirty-five degrees above zero. They were thus easily kept at a comfortable temperature by means of simple heat pumps. Towns and dwellings in the areas of volcanic activity and hot springs were now heated by steam or hot water from deep within the earth. The economic resources thus freed from the crushing burden of household heating were now used for improved libraries and schools.

Perhaps the ultimate stage in the use of the earth's heat was in the shallow, artificial ponds devoted to the culture of *Chlorella* and other protein-rich algae. These ponds were underlaid by pipes through which coursed water heated by volcanic steam. Even during the winter the algae grew, carrying on photosynthesis under the floodlights. The electricity for the banks of lights was produced by generators turned by volcanic steam. During the long days and white nights of spring, summer, and fall, the heated ponds produced a steady supply of protein-rich food supplement, for shipment to the temperate zone with its depleted and poisoned soils.

With the advent of true sustained yield from the land came the realization that this was the most important criterion of compensation for work. Thus the man responsible for the fur harvest of a particular trapline was assured a livelihood, as was his family, and as were the families of the cloudberry grower, the sawyer in the forest, the biotechnician who clipped the vegetation on the test plots in the wilderness control area, the herdsman on the moose farm, and the man who turned the hot-water valves in the *Chlorella* ponds. Sustained productivity of this sometimes harsh but always beautiful land depended on precise meshing of efforts by all the inhabitants, so that each was entitled to at least a basic share in the results.

Thus the dire predictions about the future of the Northland, made when the climatic cold-cycle began, did not materialize. There was, to be sure, a long period of difficult adjustment, but ecological reason had eventually prevailed, and the Northland with all its creatures was now self-sustaining.

Glossary

ABSCISSION LAYER—A special layer of cells at the base of a leaf petiole. This layer is the weak point at which the petiole breaks and the leaf falls.

API—Kobuk Valley (Alaska) Eskimo word denoting snow on the ground.

ARCTIC—Term used here to designate the region beyond the poleward limit of trees.

BABICHE—Narrow strips, almost threads, of raw moose or caribou skin, used for the netting in snowshoes.

CANOPY—The elevated, intermingled branches of forest trees.

CARNASSIAL—In mammals which are specialized for meat-eating, the upper fourth premolar and the lower first molar. These teeth are bladelike and engage in a scissors action.

ECOSYSTEM—Defined by Eugene P. Odum as "Any area of nature that includes living organisms and nonliving substances interacting to produce an exchange of material between the living and nonliving parts . . . to form a system."

HEAT SINK—A body or region capable of unlimited absorption of radiant energy.

HIEMAL THRESHOLD—That time in autumn when the snow cover reaches a thickness of 15 or 20 centimeters and thus offers insulation to the soil sufficient to dampen the short-term fluctuations in soil temperature.

HYDRIC—Word used in reference to the processes of ecological succession from open water toward dry land.

KITCHEN MIDDEN—The heap of cone scales discarded by squirrels during their feeding.

KLA—Athapaskan word for "hunting partner" or the social system of hunting partners.

MOR—In forest soils, a humus layer of unincorporated organic material which is distinctly differentiated from the mineral soil.

PERMAFROST—Any substratum (i.e., sand, gravel, soil, bedrock, etc.) which remains frozen for two or more years in succession.

PODZOL—A type of soil, found in regions of relatively cool, humid climates and under forest vegetation. Such soils are characterized by depletion of bases, development of acidity and the formation of eluvial A and illuvial B horizons.

PUKAK—Kobuk Valley (Alaska) Eskimo word for the fragile, latticelike layer of enlarged snow crystals found at the base of a mature snow cover.

QALI—Kobuk Valley (Alaska) Eskimo word for the snow that collects on trees.

QAMANIQ—Kobuk Valley (Alaska) Eskimo word for the deep bowl-shaped depressions in a snow cover, which form in the snow shadow around the bases of coniferous trees.

RADIATION SHIELD—A structure or device that impedes the flow of radiant heat energy.

RETICULUM—A network or meshlike structure.

RUT—The period of courtship and mating, especially in ungulates.

SERAL—Adjective referring to the seres or stages in plant succession.

SOLIFLUCTION—The slow downslope flow of saturated soil, often started by frost action.

SUBARCTIC—Term used here to denote the region between the poleward timberline and the southern limit of discontinuous permafrost; it encompasses the forest-tundra and the northern parts of the taiga.

SUBLIMATION—The physical process of a substance changing from a solid to a gas without passing through a liquid state.

SUBNIVEAN—Below the snow cover.

TAIGA—The boreal coniferous forest.

THERMOKARST—A land surface pitted by the collapse of underground caverns formed when permafrost thawed.

TUNDRA—The treeless region beyond the poleward limit of trees.

VIBRISSAE—Elongated, specialized sensory hairs in the facial region.

Epilogue

W hen I thought about how to bring up to date some of the ideas expressed in the original 1967 and 1983 editions of this book I found I could not decide. Since the mid-1960s the rate of ecosystem degradation in the northern forests has increased dramatically. While there is great public concern about the environmental changes that have taken place in the Arctic tundra, and several organizations concern themselves with publicizing the changes and lobby against such threats, there exists a remarkable lack of public concern, or awareness, about the really spectacular changes that have occurred in the taiga.

Undoubtedly the most dramatic visible change, one with far-reaching effects, has been the vast flooding in central Labrador that occurred as part of the Churchill Falls (Grand Falls) hydroelectric development. A large number of small dams and dykes has turned the great central depression of Labrador into a catchment basin to collect the water from which it is sent through the turbines buried under the now-dry Grand Falls. A significant portion of the forest-tundra and taiga of Labrador has been lost. But would a new "story" about loss of caribou habitat in Labrador be of higher priority than one about the loss of beaver and moose habitat on the other side of the peninsula? Here the James Bay hydroelectric development has destroyed significant areas of taiga. Moreover, the human loss here is severe because the clever white man once again pulled the wool over the Indians' eyes with the James Bay "settlement," wherein the James Bay Cree approved flooding of parts of their land in exchange for a sum of money they later realized was ridiculously small in relation to the vast loss of renewable resources.

Would I be justified in dramatizing these events in preference to writing about the flooding of Southern Indian Lake and the accompanying loss of the rich fishery there, and the biological loss of the Churchill River in northern Manitoba? Are these events more ecologically degrading then the effects of the Bennett Dam on the Athabaska marshes?

These changes are spectacular but are probably of less long-term importance than the effects of acid rain, wildfire and clear-cutting. Most of the concern, and research, on acid rain refer to the effects on lakes and fish. Much less concern has been shown for the fact that acid rain kills lichens, especially arboreal lichens. Woodland caribou, whose survival is closely tied to the presence of arboreal lichens, are already in a precarious situation over most of their range in Canada. They are secretive and live in scattered bands. Calculations of their numbers vary widely, and indication of how little we know about them. Acid rain also affects the lichens of the more northerly wintering ranges of the migratory Barren Ground caribou.

Of similar effect are fires. It has become fashionable in recent years to talk about fires being "good for the forest," releasing nutrients and rejuvenating the land. Such ideas may have some validity in southern regions but are not valid for the taiga. Fire degrades the taiga ecosystem. In Manitoba a series of very dry, fire-prone years unfortunatley coincided with the short tenure in office of a provincial government ideologically committed to "free enterprise" which cancelled an order for a new water bomber and which ruthlessly devastated the government air service and left the remnant helpless in the face of massive forest fires. The huge Wallace Lake and Porcupine Mountains burns in summer 1980 destroyed great areas of forest (approximately 70,000 hectares) and significantly degraded the total taiga ecosystem in Manitoba. The effects of these fires on woodland caribou began to become evident only after five years passed.

The practice of clear-cutting continues unabated all across Canada. Clear-cutting has no ecological basis; the only justification is the ease with which profits accrue to the processors of the wood or fibre. At the heart of the clear-cutting system are the large machines which require furious cutting activity in order to recoup their cost. The speed and magnitude of this operation dictate that the cutting process be completely non-selective. The direct result of clear-cutting is the loss of habitat for woodland caribous, marten, fisher and other species. The stages of vegetational recovery from clear-cutting can offer good habitat for moose and whitetail deer. But deer can carry "brain worm," a parasite to which they are immune but which is deadly to moose and caribou. An insidious, long-term effect of clear-cutting is the substitution of uniform-aged monocultures of trees instead of the original complex stands of several species of many different-aged individuals. Once again the ecosystem is simplified and degraded, as well as being put in a choice condition for insect or disease outbreaks.

There has also been an increasing tendency for governments to assume responsibility for access roads, reforestation and fire control, rather than requiring that those who take the natural harvest also manage its immediate and long-term regeneration, repair and protection. This system has a built-in financial weakness. Control and repair of exploitation damage are left to

177

the public purse, rather than being paid out of the profits reaped by those who consumed the resource. The quality of the protection service is dependent, therefore, on circumstances entirely unrelated to the damage inflicted initially.

In recent years some outright regressive measures have been instituted, such as "game ranching." I formerly championed the ides of domestication or "game ranching" of native ungulates of the taiga—moose and caribou. I know it is theoretically possible, but I believe it could be ecologically justified only under an economic and social system entirely different from that prevailing in Canada and Alaska today. If the system were under local control of native people with the meat, skins and parts destined for their own use or exchange, without being exported to the south (as their oil, minerals and wood are now) then it would be justified. I changed my mind after experiencing for two years the effects of the gross ecosystem simplification that has occurred in northern Scandinavia, especially Finland. This simplification seems to be a necessary part of the domesticated reindeer industry. *All* potential predators, competitors or possible competitors of the reindeer are eliminated—wolves, bears, wolverines, lynx, fox, eagles, even marten and ravens—because they "might hurt the reindeer." Consequently there is no wild fur industry in these regions, as a source of support for the native peoples. One can ski for many kilometres and see no sign of carnivores, large or small. Tourist advertisements do, indeed, extol the "wilderness" experience of northern Scandinavia, and, for a tourist from the crowded, polluted countryside of West Germany or Italy, the possible sight of a hare or the rare fox is a thrill. To a biologist familiar with ecosystems complete with carnivores the land of the domestic reindeer is a biological desert. We can only deplore the short-sighted attempts to "game ranch" wapiti, deer, moose or reindeer in Canada.

It is clear that we need a complete reversal of priorities and direction in the economic system for the taiga. Ecosystem stability must be the prime criterion and local human need the nest, with quick profit a minor consideration and profit to southern regions not considered at all. Efforts to achieve the short-sighted and naive goal of "national energy self-sufficiency" are anti-ecological and should be stopped. The proponents of this idea forget that the nation that retains its nonrenewable energy resources the longest will be the one that itself survives the longest. In our ecological context, the rush to exploit the finite stocks of northern energy resources for export to the south is having effects on ecosystem stability. The direct effects are severe, but undoubtedly of even greater importance are the indirect effects, especially improved access to hitherto-unexploited areas and population of animals by natives and southerners alike. Improved access might be harmless at some future time, but at present we lack sufficient cultural maturity to cope with it.

All of these reasons pale in the face of the future effects on the taiga that are inherent in the so-called "free trade" arrangement with the USA introduced by the present quisling neo-conservative government in Ottawa. This deal, which actually has little to do with trade as such, entails loss of sovereignty over enviornmental matters and, moreover, actually forces increased exploitation and extraction of both renewable and non-renewable resources in Canada.

"Vision of the Future" is now more valid than ever as a goal, especially the requirement for some ecological education for legislators. To this must now be added the necessity of ecological training for native people. The prevailing idea in the south is that the northern Indian and Inuit are master ecologists and wildlife managers. This is a false idea. Some of the elders may indeed remember strictures, taboos and patterns of behaviour that had origins in basic ecology. We must face the unfortunate fact tht most of the indigenous northern human population of today has grown up on the same cultural diet that has nourished those of us from the south: one that glorifies exploitation, individual aggrandizement and unthinking use of wildlife for personal pleasure. The freedom to hunt at any time, claimed as a treaty right by status Indians, combined with their antagonism to reporting numbers and sexes of animals taken, means that the basic data for management and conservation of any species are lacking. In effect, there is no wildlife management in Canada today wherever treaty Indians hunt. This unrestrained, unreported and unrecorded use of wildlife by the burgeoning population of native people in Canada is without doubt the most pressing problem today affecting survival of large, northern mammals.

So many of the problems facing animals of the North today lie not in the realms of biology or technical wildlife management or even science in general, but in politics. Technically we know what to do, or at least, what *not* to do. The problem lies in the transfer of knowledge from scientist to politician, and the translation of this knowledge into action, regulation, enforcement and change of public attitudes. If I were to expand *Wild Harmony* that is where I would have to go, into the realm of human politics.

WILLIAM O. PRUITT, JR.
Winnipeg, Manitoba
May 20, 1988